MW00843303

Mentoris Project
745 South Sierra Madre Drive
San Marino, CA 91108

Cover photo courtesy of Becker Medical Library, Washington University School of Medicine

Cover design: Suzanne Turpin

More information at www.mentorisproject.org

ISBN: 978-1-947431-36-2

Library of Congress Control Number: 2021937077

All net proceeds from the sale of this book will be donated to the Mentoris Project whose mission is to support educational initiatives that foster an appreciation of history and culture to encourage and inspire young people to create a stronger future.

The Mentoris Project is a series of novels and biographies about the lives of great men and women who have changed history through their contributions as scientists, inventors, explorers, thinkers, and creators. The Barbera Foundation sponsors this series in the hope that, like a mentor, each book will inspire the reader to discover how she or he can make a positive contribution to society.

Contents

Foreword

First and foremost, Mentor was a person. We tend to think of the word *mentor* as a noun (a mentor) or a verb (to mentor), but there is a very human dimension embedded in the term. Mentor appears in Homer's *Odyssey* as the old friend entrusted to care for Odysseus's household and his son Telemachus during the Trojan War. When years pass and Telemachus sets out to search for his missing father, the goddess Athena assumes the form of Mentor to accompany him. The human being welcomes a human form for counsel. From its very origins, becoming a mentor is a transcendent act; it carries with it something of the holy.

The Mentoris Project sets out on an Athena-like mission: We hope the books that form this series will be an inspiration to all those who are seekers, to those of the twenty-first century who are on their own odysseys, trying to find enduring principles that will guide them to a spiritual home. The stories that comprise the series are all deeply human. These books dramatize the lives of great men and women whose stories bridge the ancient and the modern, taking many forms, just as Athena did, but always holding up a light for those living today.

Whether in novel form or traditional biography, these books

plumb the individual characters of our heroes' journeys. The power of storytelling has always been to envelop the reader in a vivid and continuous dream, and to forge a link with the subject. Our goal is for that link to guide the reader home with a new inspiration.

What is a mentor? A guide, a moral compass, an inspiration. A friend who points you toward true north. We hope that the Mentoris Project will become that friend, and it will help us all transcend our daily lives with something that can only be called holy.

—Robert J. Barbera, Founder, The Mentoris Project
—Ken LaZebnik, Founding Editor, The Mentoris Project

To my mentors Northrop Frye and
Marshall McLuhan, with gratitude

"Imagination is more important than knowledge."

—ALBERT EINSTEIN

Prologue

THE NOBEL PRIZE

Stockholm, December 10, 1986. The Nobel Prize in Physiology or Medicine is awarded to Rita Levi-Montalcini, the only Italian recipient in the last sixty years. She has traveled far: from a shy, insecure Jewish child growing up in Turin, afraid of the dark, to a self-confident scientist receiving the most prestigious recognition in her field. Her ground-breaking work has spanned two continents and half a century. It is important to her, now that she is seventy-seven years old, to be exemplary both as a scientist and a woman.

To mark this crowning achievement of a lifetime, Rita has commissioned a regal velvet dress with long sleeves in her favorite winter colors from fashion designer Roberto Capucci. The deep green, amaranth red, and purple would be the appropriate colors for the season and the occasion. Maestro Capucci, whose dresses—or rather, sculptures in cloth—are found in the world's most prominent museums, wants her to be the queen of the evening and at the same time to challenge stereotypes about scientists neglecting their physical appearance. Since all the men at the ceremony in Stockholm will be wearing black tie, he has suggested that her dress should sport tails. She is as delighted by this idea as she is by the Caravaggesque tonalities of her dress.

Two months earlier, in Rome, sitting in her elegant apartment and reading Agatha Christie's *Evil Under the Sun*, she was at the point of discovering the identity of the murderer when the telephone rang. It was the Karolinska Institute in Stockholm announcing that she had won the most coveted scientific prize in the world and that the ceremony was scheduled for December 10. She was so surprised and overwhelmed that she dropped the novel to sit down at her book-covered desk, trying to process this extraordinary news. It had all begun with her free-thinking parents, Adamo and Adele, settling in Turin, a city rich in culture and industry, once renowned for its religious tolerance. Had they still been alive, she would have dearly loved to show them, particularly her father, what she had made of her life. In spite of her outstanding aptitude for study, he had prevented his daughter's attendance at a school that would allow her to go on to university. How right she had been to insist on going her own way.

She saw, in a flash, the siblings she loved. Gino, the renowned architect and sculptor, was also no longer alive. When she was a little girl, she had wanted to be like him, to express herself professionally and become financially independent. Then there was Anna, her literary sister, who gave up her aspirations as a writer to dedicate herself to her husband and children. Lastly, she came to her twin sister, Paola, the painter, whose aesthetic sensibility she fully shared.

Once she had hung up the phone, Rita wanted to be alone for a few hours, revisiting all the battles she had fought and obstacles she had overcome in order to do the work she loved: studying the nervous system in all its cellular complexity. Growing up as a Jewish girl in a patriarchal and Christian-centered milieu had been difficult enough, but by the time she reached the age of thirty, her very existence had become endangered. Because of the fascist racial laws of 1938 and the vicious spread of anti-Semitism, she had been painfully deprived of her teaching position at the University of Turin, where she had graduated summa cum laude in Medicine and Surgery under the outstanding histologist Giuseppe Levi. They had become very close during the fascist era, sharing the same destiny of being persecuted Jews. What a pity he had died without the satisfaction of learning how his pupil had succeeded in a way totally independent of her master. He would have been so proud to learn that, along with two of his other students, Salvador Luria and Renato Dulbecco, she too had earned the world's highest scientific recognition.

But that had been an undreamed-of possibility to the twenty-nine-year-old scientist in 1938. Stripped of her job and position, she had to work in hiding while German armies spread destruction and death throughout Europe. As a woman, a Jew, and a scientist in an almost exclusively male preserve, she was severely disadvantaged; nevertheless, she chose to be faithful to her vocation, investing her energy in cultivating the life of the mind in the tiny laboratory she managed to rig up in her bedroom. Her neuroscientific investigations on chick embryos were an ideal home project because eggs were still available and inexpensive. All she had to purchase was her treasured binocular microscope, which she took with her whenever sirens signaled the need to flee to air raid shelters. She bought it on December 10, 1940. What a coincidence that she would be receiving her prize on this day!

One of the things that kept her going was an intriguing scientific article she happened to come across. Written by embryologist Viktor Hamburger at Washington University in St. Louis, Missouri, a refugee from Nazi Germany and a pioneer in the field of developmental neurobiology, this article became her bible and inspiration. Patiently and courageously, she pursued detailed experiments in her improvised and rudimentary lab, dissecting embryos and investigating neurons in depth with Levi.

At last, when the Anglo-American allies freed Italy from the Nazi invaders, she was able to reclaim her identity. In 1947 her curiosity and daring led her to accept an invitation from Professor Hamburger himself to spend some time in St. Louis. Instead of staying for a semester or two at Washington University, she ended up starting a new life there at the age of thirty-eight. It was a courageous decision to commit herself to an existence in a foreign country—she knew only some basic English at the time—far from home and family. Rita was looking for a radical change and had no time to waste. She was strongly motivated by her desire to regain the decade she had lost. Working with the respected Professor Hamburger, she had nothing to lose and everything to gain.

Serendipity also played a role in her transformation into an esteemed scientist with a solid reputation. In 1951, purely by chance, she came across a brief article by Elmer Bueker, one of Hamburger's former students, stating that he had introduced bits of mouse tumor into a chick embryo, triggering an abnormally high growth of nerve cells. Immensely struck by this information, she repeated the same experiment over and over, until she found to her amazement a new research path clearly opening in front of her. In her letters to her mother and Paola, she hinted at an extraordinary scientific possibility. She knew that her compelling intuitions were more typical of an artist than a scientist. After all, she was the sister of a painter and of a sculptor.

That same year at the New York Academy of Science symposium, the influential scholar Paul Weiss had acknowledged her finding in very flattering terms. As she left the symposium that evening, her discovery suddenly appeared to her as a twinkling little star indicating the way to a cave full of treasures as in *One Thousand and One Nights*.[1]

Her self-assurance was growing by leaps and bounds; she was proud of being recognized as "the Italian scientist" wherever she went. It was less than two decades since Mussolini's *Fascist Manifesto* had proclaimed her—along with all the Jews living in Italy—as "not belonging to the Italian race." And how ironic that in the United States she felt more fully recognized as an Italian in her own right than she did at home.

From Turin to St. Louis—what a trajectory! And at a time

when there was yet no commercial air travel, no TV, no computers or cellphones, only one landline at Washington University, from which to call or to be called. Yet she hadn't stopped there. In order to obtain the final evidence for her hypothesis, to identify from a chemical perspective the mysterious fluid making nerve cells grow exponentially, she traveled to Brazil. She had always wanted to see the beauties of South America, but the real goal of this journey was to perform experiments in vitro in her friend Hertha Meyer's laboratory at the Institute of Biophysics in Rio de Janeiro. Here her analysis confirmed again and again what she had guessed in vivo in St. Louis. How not to remember the following six most intense years of her career back in St. Louis but side by side with Stanley Cohen, such a talented biochemist? It was with him that her "wonder molecule" was identified and called nerve growth factor, or simply NGF, the molecule of life.[2]

And finally, how gratifying to share, thirty-five years later, science's most coveted prize with her young associate!

Stanley had been woken up in the middle of the night in Tennessee by a call from Stockholm's Karolinska Institute. He must have been as surprised and delighted as Rita that he had been awarded a Nobel Prize for the discovery of epidermal growth factor (EGF), the protein molecule so closely connected with NGF.

Having indulged herself reviewing and reliving these key events of her adventurous life, Rita turned her attention to the press conference scheduled for the following morning. How fortunate she had been to be gifted, like her father, with a strong personality and determination, but at the same time to be given the tools, the freedom, and the assistance indispensable to solving the great scientific puzzle that led her to the Nobel.

She was amused to remember the letter she sent to her family back in 1959, when the research she was doing with Stanley was at its most intense. She wrote that after having had guests for dinner, she was at last able to transform the table back into a writing desk. There, her imagination would unleash ideas with such fecundity that she had only to "catch them and pin them down to the paper." She concluded by declaring that if she ever got a Nobel Prize, it would be thanks to her special desk. She playfully made her mother and her twin, Paola, her alter ego, privy to her most secret hope.[3]

Tonight Paola would help her celebrate, not with caviar and champagne, but with a frugal meal of broth and Chinese rice, treasuring each intimate moment they could spend together before the journalists invaded. She fully intended to keep working and researching as she had always done. Rita would go to bed at 11:00 p.m. and get up around 5:00 a.m., sticking to her daily routine, Nobel Prize or not.

The next day she received the first group of journalists and commented that she was particularly happy because when she first started her research on the nervous system, her field of interest did not seem to have any future. Only after NGF had been discovered did she begin to believe in the importance of her findings, which went on to exponentially widen their sphere of influence, gradually contributing not only to basic science, but also to the very future of medicine.

The Nobel Committee announced their motivation for

granting the award: "The discovery of nerve growth factor (NGF) in the beginning of the 1950s is a fascinating example of how a skilled observer can create a concept out of apparent chaos." Before then, neurologists had only very vague ideas about the functioning of neurological cells and circuits. Rita Levi-Montalcini had brought into view something that had been there all along, yet had never before been noticed.

In subsequent years, the concept that started as a hunch became an established reality, a foundational concept in science and medicine.[4]

Interestingly enough, Rita had just concluded her forth-coming autobiography, *In Praise of Imperfection: My Life and Work*, not with a final statement, but with a humble question:

> *Will the NGF . . . now no longer collected from neoplastic tissues or from the mouths of snakes and mice but aseptically distilled in the laboratory—be able to bring back order to the functionally impaired neuronal circuitries of that immensely complex entity, the brain of* Homo sapiens?[5]

On December 6, Rita was at Fiumicino airport, ready to depart with most of her relatives and her closest collaborators, Luigi Aloe and Pietro Calissano. Luigi felt particularly honored to be in charge of the whole trip and schedule. They were welcomed at the Stockholm airport by the Italian ambassador and the Swedish Vice-Minister of the Interior, and stayed for a week at the Grand Hotel. Every day, piles of telegrams of congratulations were delivered along with the most beautiful flower arrangements. An intense sequence of meetings, lectures, and symposia quickly filled the agenda.

The following day at the press conference at the Karolinska Institute, the Nobel Assembly pointed out that Rita was only the fourth woman to receive the Nobel Prize in Physiology or Medicine, after Gerty Cori in 1947, Rosalyn Yalow in 1977, and Barbara McClintock in 1983, and specified the compelling reasons why Rita Levi-Montalcini and Stanley Cohen were to be awarded the prize:

> *The discovery of NGF and EGF has opened new fields of widespread importance to basic science. As a direct consequence we may increase our understanding of many disease states such as developmental malformations, degenerative changes in senile dementia, delayed wound healing and tumour diseases. The characterization of these growth factors is therefore expected, in the near future, to result in the development of new therapeutic agents and improved treatment in various clinical diseases.*[6]

Their statement also highlighted that:

> *In the research area of growth factors and their biological action, Levi-Montalcini and Cohen have created a scientific school with an increasing number of followers. All*

research groups who discovered 'new' growth factors have however just followed in the tracks of Levi-Montalcini and Cohen.

The ceremony took place in the monumental Konserthuset after a memorable performance of Prokofiev's Symphony No. 1 in D Major, in the presence of the royal couple and 1,400 guests. When Rita came down the stairs, arm in arm with King Carl XVI Gustaf of Sweden, she was radiant. She was wearing a dress suitable for a coronation, and indeed that night she was being crowned for her scientific achievements by the king himself.

Rita, so diminutive and frail-looking but with a regal demeanor, mounted the stage to receive the Nobel in Physiology or Medicine, the gold medal that only three Italians had managed to attain before her: Camillo Golgi, Salvador Luria, and Renato Dulbecco. Three out of four had come from the same city, Turin, and the same tutelage of Giuseppe Levi. What an incomparable tribute to her great master that was!

For the first time ever, the Karolinska Institute allowed children to attend the ceremony. Along with her brother Gino's widow, Maria Gattone, and their children, Piera and Emanuele, there were also the two granddaughters, Paola and eight-year-old Claudia. Family had always been important for Rita, and this was the main reason why she had returned to Italy a few years before she retired from Washington University, to start a new productive stage in her life.

She held a soft leather folder containing her acceptance speech, but, gifted with a prodigious memory, she did not need to read a single line. The magic of her dress was enhanced by the shimmering tonalities of the velvet and made a startling contrast to the yellow carnations, a gift from Sanremo, the city where Alfred Nobel had died in 1896. Outside it was snowing.

After introducing the award recipients, Professor Kerstin Hall, an endocrinologist from the Karolinska Hospital in Stockholm, invited the two laboratory partners and friends to step forward and receive the Nobel Prize from the hands of His Majesty the King. In the history of Italy, only one woman before Rita had been granted this great recognition: Grazia Deledda, in the field of Literature (1926). Rita returned to her seat accompanied by a ceremonial fanfare of trumpets.

One of the deepest goals of Rita's existence had been accomplished: the seemingly endless search for and discovery of the infinitesimal part of the truth surrounding the great mystery represented by the human mind—the molecule of life.

A gala dinner for all the distinguished guests followed at Stockholm City Hall, a huge space surrounded by classical columns evoking the atmosphere of an Italian piazza, designed by Ragnar Östberg. Rita, being the only woman awarded the Nobel Prize that year, was asked to sit on the right side of the king. Not far from her were Silvia, Queen of Sweden, wearing a gold tiara studded with diamonds and amethysts, which had belonged to Napoleon's first wife, Giuseppina; and Nigerian writer and playwright Wole Soyinka, the first Black Nobel Prize winner for Literature. Forty-three chefs prepared the dinner, which included salmon mousse in shrimp sauce as an appetizer and moose filet with leeks and morels as main course, and concluded with the celebrated "Nobel semifreddo," topped with a large chocolate "N" sprinkled with edible gold leaf. After the master of ceremonies had rung a tiny golden bell, an army of waiters in white livery placed all the plates on the table simultaneously. After the speeches, the guests, along with the royal couple, moved to the nearby Golden Hall covered in glittering mosaics, where the orchestra of the Conservatory of Stockholm started playing a waltz to invite everyone to dance.[7]

When Rita's autobiography was published, she had made no explicit mention of her Nobel Prize. She concluded her book just as she had her lecture that evening in Stockholm, consistently downplaying her own role while generously acknowledging the collaboration of other researchers. She emphasized that scientists should not be afraid of going beyond the given facts and boldly venture into the unknown.

Difficulties did not exist for her. She always shrugged them off like "a duck shaking the water off its wings."[8]

Rita was deeply touched when her close friend, writer Primo Levi, immediately commented on the announcement of her Nobel Prize in the Turin daily newspaper *La Stampa*, on October 14, 1986:

Finally, a moment of uncontaminated joy. Joy because after too many years, the most coveted prize in medicine has been awarded to a woman—and from Turin. Because this woman from Turin honours me with her friendship. And because the Nobel Prize fits Rita like a key does a keyhole. It is finally a prize for a life fruitfully dedicated to science, a prize received by the hands of a tiny lady with an indomitable will and the bearing of a princess, who is still pursuing the same goals with the energy of a genius and that rare combination of patience and impatience, typical of great innovators.

Rita is not walking towards the sunset: for her the Nobel does not represent the conquests of the past. Even today among a number of unresolved difficulties, her activity is relentless.

Rita is not only working behind the microscope in the lab but she is always looking for new collaborators and students to continue in her field of research, while travelling throughout the world to illustrate the deep meaning of her research to other scholars and to a larger public. It is not up to me to judge her findings but I think I can guess how valid they are, through friends and competitors: they are creative and they constitute a barrier that has been broken, creating a vital opening through which a new light leads to the most evanescent awareness: that the human mind can understand itself.[9]

Chapter One

GROWING UP IN A JEWISH FAMILY IN TURIN

In the first decade of the twentieth century, Turin was an important and prosperous industrial and cultural center in northern Italy, the equal of Milan and Genoa. In fact, throughout the twentieth century, Turin has functioned as a major European crossroads for industry, commerce, and trade. The capital of the Piedmont region, Turin, lies along the banks of the Po, the longest river in Italy, and is fringed by the western chain of the Alps. Turin is sometimes called "the cradle of Italian liberty and tolerance" for having been the birthplace and home of notable individuals who contributed to the Risorgimento—the movement that led to the unification of Italy—such as Camillo Benso, Count of Cavour. When the country was first united in 1861, Turin became Italy's capital for four years under King Victor Emmanuel II of Savoy. Under the Savoyard royal family, Turin was liberal and tolerant toward the Jewish community, unlike other parts of Europe.

Rita Levi-Montalcini was born there on April 22, 1909, the youngest of four children, and was raised in an upper-class Jewish family whose genealogical tree went back to the fourteenth century, in particular on her mother's side, whose family originally settled in Montalcino at the time of the Republic of Siena. Their apartment on the fourth floor of a handsome nineteenth-century building overlooked the tall plane trees of a large avenue leading to a nearby square where the gigantic bronze statue of Victor Emmanuel II was a towering presence. Most of the year the family lived in Turin, moving in the summer, with maid, governess, and chauffeur, to their house in the Asti hills, where Turin's wealthy migrated to spend the hotter months.

Rita's mother, Adele, was a talented artist while her father, Adamo, was an electrical engineer and gifted mathematician. Rita grew up in a loving and culturally engaged environment with two sisters, Paola and Anna, nicknamed Nina, and one brother, Gino.

While her twin sister, Paola, with her lively blue eyes, resembled their father in disposition and looks, Rita was the living image of her maternal grandmother with her pensive, gray-green eyes and melancholic gaze. As Rita herself pointed out in her autobiography, their looks were as different as their characters, yet no two sisters could have been closer. From an early age, Paola showed great talent as an artist, an ability she may have inherited from her mother—a gift that Rita admired unconditionally, knowing that it was one she lacked herself. In fact, she had no idea where her true abilities lay until she reached her early twenties.[10]

Rita was shy and insecure while her twin sister was extroverted and gregarious. She had no self-confidence and was terrified of the dark, of any evil presence, real or imagined, and curiously of anything mechanical, like wind-up toys. After dusk in their preschool days, she would always ask Paola to accompany her to the bathroom, since there was a long, dark corridor in their apartment connecting the bedrooms to the playroom. Rita was a vulnerable child in need of protection. Her father used to call her "my shrinking violet." However, at the same time, she was also "very strong inside," as her mother always maintained, and as she herself would admit later on.

Throughout their lives, the twins had a very special bond. They had established a unique empathy since they were children, which excluded the intrusion of third parties, such as their brother, Gino, who was seven years older, and Nina, who was five years older than the two of them. This barrier inevitably fell during adolescence because the siblings' differences in age were neutralized by cultural affinities. On several occasions Rita called Paola "a part of myself" and yet later on, while still caring deeply for each other, they fostered a great freedom and independence.

Rita had the same reserved character as her mother. She had a natural reluctance to engage in physical contact. She loved her father, but always tried to avoid kissing him because of his prickly moustache and would send him an aerial good-night kiss. Even though she had no difficulty in kissing her mother because of her soft skin, she really preferred blowing kisses to her as well. Rita and Paola were looked after and taken to school by a series of governesses. Their favorite, Giovanna, was like a second mother and confidante.

Rita's interest in literature was fostered by her older sister. They shared a deep love for Nordic sagas, especially *Gösta Berling*, a novel by Selma Lagerlöf, the first female winner of the Nobel Prize for Literature. As children, in fact, both girls dreamt of becoming writers themselves. A love for literature persisted in Rita, whose later reading ranged from Ludovico Ariosto to William Butler Yeats, from Primo Levi to Lawrence Ferlinghetti. Yet Nina, by consenting to marry a gentleman chosen by the family, embodied her parents' ideals at the expense of pursuing her literary passions. The Levis were convinced that the primary vocation of a woman was to marry and bear children. Rita and Paola were expected to follow Nina's example.

In adolescence Rita became very close to her brother, whom she admired for his strong artistic personality. Gino was very talented in drawing and modeling clay, with aspirations to become an artist, an ambition thwarted by Adamo. Father and son reached a compromise and Gino pursued a degree in architecture while continuing to foster his deep love of sculpture. He was to become one of Italy's prominent postwar architects, along with close friend Giuseppe Pagano, a major exponent of twentieth-century structural rationalism.[11] Gino represented everything Rita aspired to—a university education and a profession that provided intellectual and financial independence.

Even though from early childhood Rita was closer to her

mother, her father left a pervasive influence on her life. She inherited his tenacity, ingenuity, and work ethic, as well as his radical free thinking. Adamo's personality was formed by the cheerful and carefree environment of his large family, where everyone from early childhood had a decided character. Adamo, having lost his own father at the age of nine, considered his uncle-stepfather, "Il Barba," the dominant figure in his life. Apparently Il Barba wanted to make a rabbi out of Adamo, but eventually had to accept his aversion to such a vocation.

Rita was raised as a secular Jew, tolerant of all creeds. Like most Italian Jews at the time, the Levis had Catholic friends and were well integrated into Italian society. Adamo, a Sephardic Jew, rarely attended synagogue but did not deny his family's roots. He always told his children that if they were asked about their faith to say that they were "free thinkers" and as adults would be able to choose their religion. His secular values came into conflict with his extended family. At major Jewish celebrations such as Passover and Yom Kippur, he would openly voice his disapproval of strict adherence to the Scriptures, which would inevitably aggravate Rita's sense of uneasiness and isolation. She and her siblings tried to ignore the scornful glances of their cousins, but the open conflict with Aunt Anna, Rita's step-grandmother, provoked great suffering.

Even as a child, Rita found herself inhabiting a tiny island of free thinkers. She was invited to witness rituals such as fasting, but not to participate, because of their father's presence. She and her siblings were allowed to help themselves to the traditional reward for fasting, *bruscadelle*—toasted bread flavored with cinnamon and spices, soaked in sweet wine—that they loved so much, but only after their cousins, who had indeed fasted, had fully satisfied their appetites.[12]

Rita attended a nearby elementary school. Girls were separated from boys in different classes. The majority attending the school were from working-class or lower-middle-class families. Rita's parents decided that their children should not attend a private school for the privileged classes only, run by a religious order, but instead a public school that included all social levels.

Rita retained only pleasant memories of the years spent at the elementary school, especially of her teacher, who was very gifted and dedicated to her pupils. She instilled in Rita an appreciation of the immense cultural heritage of Italy and a passionate love for her country. When Italy entered the First World War, Rita and her classmates followed day by day the furious battles on the Carso and in other areas of the Friuli-Venezia Giulia region. Rita reached the point of declaring that she loved the King and Queen of Italy first, followed by her parents. Her patriotic sentiments were boosted by the fact that her beloved teacher's sister, a Red Cross nurse, was often on duty at the front. Rita's admiration was so great that she hoped the war would last long enough so that she too could become a Red Cross nurse and do something heroic, but luckily this did not happen.[13]

Later on in life, Rita wrote a handbook for young students, maintaining that elementary education is most important because it introduces children into human society, forging their minds and characters. It requires very skilled teachers who understand how capable and receptive children are at this stage and who teach the intellectual equality of the sexes. Moreover, education methods should be neither authoritarian nor permissive, but strictly cognitive. The mental potential of children should not be underestimated, and they should be engaged and stimulated from birth in a dialectically active rather than meekly passive learning process.[14]

Chapter Two

REBELLING AGAINST A PATRIARCHAL SOCIETY

R ita and her two sisters attended a school that did not qualify them for a university education. Their father made this decision not because he wanted to save money or because he lacked faith in the intelligence of his daughters, but because he was truly convinced that any professional life for a woman was incompatible with the duties of a wife and of a mother. Rita was the only one dissatisfied with the high school she was forced to attend, and once she got her diploma, she felt she was in a blind alley. The Victorian age had ended with the beginning of the twentieth century, yet its views on education continued to determine the roles of the sexes. In a lecture included in *Sesame and Lilies*, art critic and writer John Ruskin, one of the most influential thinkers of the second half of the nineteenth century, observed:

> *The man's power is active, progressive, defensive. He is*

eminently the doer, the creator, the discoverer, the defender.
His intellect is for speculation and invention; his energy for
adventure, for war, and for conquest . . . But the woman's
power is for rule, not for battle, and her intellect is not for
invention or creation, but for sweet ordering, arrangement
and decision.[15]

Rita was raised in an atmosphere where her father's will prevailed, "unchallenged in decisions large and small."[16] Her parents had met on January 10, 1901, when Adele was only twenty-one and Adamo was thirty-three. He was passionate about opera, and every morning while shaving he would sing one of his favorite arias from Verdi's *La Traviata* in a baritone voice like Giorgio Germont's: "He who offends a woman—even if only in a fit of rage—makes himself worthy of scorn." Francesco Piave's libretto displays a formal respect for women; however, this statement comes from a father figure who single-handedly decides the dramatic destiny of his son, Alfredo, and his lover, Violetta, without considering their feelings. Even as a child, Rita was irritated by this sense of male superiority, which she could not accept.[17] While she would never contradict her father out of respect, she secretly rebelled against his prejudiced opinions to the point that later on in life she would change her name from Levi to Levi-Montalcini, proudly adding her mother's maiden name.

Adamo's sense of male entitlement—he was nicknamed "Damino the Terrible"—did not, however, prevent him from sincerely admiring the intelligence of his younger sister, Costanza, known as Aunt Tina, who had a great gift for music and mathematics, and started a new career as a sculptor when she was over sixty. He also had great respect for his other sister, Gabriella, who pursued a university education, earning a doctoral degree in literature. Nonetheless, he missed no occasion to stress that both women had encountered big problems balancing their professional lives with maternal duties. Therefore, he had decided that his daughters should receive only a basic education, attending the girls' high school, which offered no possibility of access to university. Adamo's ruling had no serious consequences for Rita's two sisters, Nina and Paola. Nina, though skilled in mathematics, was determined to become a writer and therefore thought she did not need a specific degree to express herself. Paola's exceptional artistic talents led her to finish high school with excellent grades and then to train under painter Felice Casorati. Later, she was privileged to be endorsed by artist Giorgio de Chirico, who was also born in the same "monarchic and fluvial" city of Turin.[18]

The one who suffered the most from this unilateral male decision was Rita. She did not have any scientific training in high school and was not particularly attracted to sports. For a while she considered studying philosophy, then realized she wasn't logically minded enough. Encouraged by Nina's advice, she considered a career in writing, but was dissatisfied with her efforts. At whatever cost, she had to find a way out of the labyrinth.

As fate would have it, Ariadne's thread, as Rita admitted,

was literally "put into her hand" by the tragic illness of one of the three women in her life she loved most: Giovanna, her governess, who, along with her mother and Aunt Anna, represented her three guardian angels.

Giovanna came from Rivarossa, a small village in Piedmont, about an hour's drive from Turin, and had been hired before the twins were born. She had weathered a childhood of privation and suffering, forced by her rigid father, a peasant, to get up at four o'clock every morning to feed the few animals they owned. She was the third of five sisters and her mother died giving birth to her fifth child. Giovanna was a Catholic, but she never raised the question of religion with the girls or tried to convert them, as previous governesses had done. Unlike her oldest sister, Caterina, she was not a fanatic, and unlike her younger sister Bettina, she was not overly talkative or contemptuous but maintained a nunlike reserve.

She was very attached to Adele and had great regard for Adamo. They treated her like a member of the family, valuing her open mind, sensitivity, and availability to help at all times. Gradually, a special bond of love and reciprocal respect developed between them; it was no surprise, then, that Adele became concerned at noticing how pale and emaciated Giovanna seemed. After a thorough checkup by the family doctor, Adele was given a sealed envelope containing a diagnosis of suspected stomach cancer along with a recommendation of immediate hospital admission for emergency surgery. Unfortunately, it was too late because the cancer had spread. Giovanna went back to the family unaware of how serious her condition was, and from that moment she was spared from any chores by the whole family, who treated her with great tenderness and consideration.

Giovanna was only forty-five, and Rita could not accept the relentless advance of her lethal illness. Rita was full of shame and regret. She could not believe that while her governess had been constantly interested in the twenty-year-old's well-being, encouraging her to stop mulling over her problems and go out for a walk and breathe some fresh air, she herself had been totally blind to Giovanna's fast-deteriorating health.

Out of grief and remorse, Rita vowed to resume her studies and pursue medicine. She even personally expressed the wish to take Giovanna under her direct care. A very interesting comment unexpectedly followed on Giovanna's part: "Masnà [Piedmontese dialect for 'child'], when you are a doctor, I shall have been in the Elysian Fields for years." This showed Giovanna's sensitivity in choosing to refer to the beyond not in Catholic terms, but in a more poetic, mythological way, making "a kind of compromise between what she hoped for and what she felt lay close at hand."[19] Soon afterward, Giovanna asked to return to her native village and died there surrounded by her sisters in the little farmhouse where she was born.

The last time Rita saw her was on a cold November day in 1930. She had joined Paola, Adele, and Aunt Anna. They were driven by Carlo, Aunt Anna's driver, whom Giovanna secretly adored. She had been very attracted to him, but unfortunately he chose to marry Aunt Anna's cook, whom she detested.

Rita saw a skeletal Giovanna lying in bed, who nevertheless appreciated their visit and their encouraging words. A few days later, they all went to her funeral. Soon afterward, Rita finally knew with certainty what she wanted to do with her life. She would study medicine in defiance of what she described as "a Victorian climate, ill-suited to my natural tendencies." At this point she had decided that she was not particularly interested in marriage or having a family. Instead, she opted for "serving people" in a medical capacity. Her heart was set on a life of study and research, and she refused to play a subordinate role in a male-oriented society. With the support of her mother and older sister, she found the courage to talk to her father about her future.

Rita told Adamo that she had been attracted to the medical profession since first grade, when she had dreamt of becoming a Red Cross nurse during the war. Her father tried to warn her that, having finished high school three years earlier, she would find it a challenge to resume studying. Additionally, the field of medicine was very demanding and an unsuitable place for a woman. As he spoke, she could see from the way his nostrils were dilating how uneasy he was at having to cope with this unexpected predicament. Suddenly, to Rita's surprise, he yielded and told her that, provided she was sure of what she wanted, he would not stand in her way. For the first time, she became the protagonist of her own life.

Rita had not studied Greek, and knew very little Latin and mathematics. In the 1920s, only 70 percent of the Italian population could read, and the percentage of literate women was even lower. Together with her cousin Eugenia de Lustig, a year and a half younger, she prepared herself for a very difficult examination that would allow her entry into medical school. Rita was aware that, while they would be able to study philosophy, literature, history, and geography on their own, they both needed serious tutoring in the three most difficult subjects. They chose Professor Lobetti-Bodoni, who, besides being a family friend, was highly regarded in Turin for his ability to teach Latin and Greek. For mathematics, they selected Professor Guido Ascoli, a respected scientific high school teacher. They planned to sit for the examinations as "external candidates" for the fall session and complete their preparation in eight solid months of study. Spending the summer in the same mountain village where Professor Lobetti-Bodoni was living, the two young women rose at four o'clock every morning to go through the homework they had been assigned the previous day. While Eugenia was confident and optimistic, Rita was anxious, even though she studied hard. During the final written test, Rita swiftly managed to complete the Latin translation and had time to help a girl sitting next to her, who was struggling with the passage. Rita passed all her exams with flying colors in spite of her poor performance in geography—she had been unable to explain the Pacific Gulf currents.

The joy Rita experienced with this initial success that would allow her to realize her dreams marked a turning point in her life. It was a liberation after a subdued, silent, personal revolution. She did not run away from home or abruptly sever ties with her family. In her childhood she had unquestioningly accepted a decision that had been imposed in an authoritarian way, according to the strict principles of a firmly paternalistic society.

Only after completing high school had she begun to resent being born female and being denied the same options as her brother.

For almost three years she had felt paralyzed, not knowing what to do with herself because of the dead-end schooling she had received. She suffered so much that, later on, her generous nature led her to write several books on education to inspire young people to find their own path in life. We know now that individuals are more the result of their education and sociocultural environment than of mere genetic determination.[20] Rita pressed her readers to question the status quo and radically revise their way of thinking and acting, and to give more importance to their cognitive and rational potential. She encouraged them to become aware of the surrounding world in a spirit of service, to fight obsessive self-centeredness and preconceptions. And since all individuals are created equal and free, she emphasized the need to combat any reductive concept of the role of women in society. When Rita finally asserted her will before her father, she was not only making a personal decision about her future, but also contributing to a historical turning point by claiming rights that women had been denied for centuries. Why should two XX chromosomes continue to decide the destiny of millions of women? It was time to react and bring about change. In her book *Tempo di mutamenti* (*Time for Changes*), she urged young people to use their intellect by liberating themselves irrevocably from preconceptions and religious superstition. She championed and adopted Kant's motto: *Sapere aude!* A life without education, she insisted, is like living in a maimed body.[21]

Interestingly enough, at the time there was a popular saying in Italy that was very dear to Pope Pio X (1835–1914). It ordained that a woman should "be pleasing, keep quiet, and stay at home"—*che se piasa, che se tasa, che stia in casa.*[22] The Catholic Church saw any feminist movement as an open challenge to the traditional concept of womanly obedience and submission. Rita had also started reading a few books by Sigmund Freud and gradually came to object to some of his theories, current in the 1940s and 1950s, which in her opinion misleadingly ended up prolonging women's sense of inferiority.[23]

The sudden death of Rita's father in 1932, when she was completing her second year of medical school, filled her with regret and remorse "for having disappointed him" by becoming what *she* wanted to be rather than what *he* wanted for her. Without meaning to, father and daughter had caused each other much suffering during Rita's adolescent years. Yet he left her an indelible legacy of resilience, which was a constant inspiration. After he suffered a first stroke in May 1932, as well as occasional instances of angina pain accompanied by sudden memory lapses, Rita's mother tried to convince him to use his car to go to work. Adamo, however, insisted on public transport, claiming that the brisk morning air was good for his health. His true reason was to economize. He had been forced to close down his ice factory and alcohol distillery in Bari, on the Adriatic coast in the south, an enterprise he had bravely started at the age of twenty-one, after graduating in engineering from the Polytechnic University of Turin. The distillery grew quickly and gave work to a thousand people, but after the war, a series of setbacks and employee strikes transformed the plant's profits into growing losses. He avoided bankruptcy by seeking financial help from his three brothers-in-law. Despite adversity and the fact that he was no longer a young man, he then managed to launch a new ice factory and distillery in Turin, although at a very high price: his own life.

Adamo wanted at all costs to live for at least three more years to realize the plans he had for his businesses. During brief periods of improved health, he recited stanzas from the *Divina Commedia* in his deep voice to prove to himself that his faculties were still intact. He was surrounded by his family when he eventually died of heart failure. Rita kissed her father's forehead and thought with anguish of all the kisses she had been unable to give him in her childhood.[24] He was at least spared from witnessing Hitler's rise to power, with all the catastrophic consequences it would bring for his family and the Jewish community as a whole.

Chapter Three

THE CLASSES OF GIUSEPPE LEVI

R ita was adamant about studying medicine after passing the entrance exams, while Eugenia was at first inclined to apply to the faculty of mathematics, but in the end she opted for the same choice as Rita and never regretted it. In the fall of 1930, they both started attending the medical school of the revered University of Turin, founded in 1404. On the first day, Rita and Eugenia entered the somber amphitheater of the Institute of Anatomy, School of Medicine, where a cadaver lay on a dissecting table in the center and the apprehensive students crowded the benches of the semicircular hall. Out of more than 300 students attending Professor Giuseppe Levi's lectures, only seven were girls. The lectures always took place in the morning, and in the afternoon they both did laboratory work. Rita was particularly interested in anatomy, the study of the body's structure. Of all the body's mechanisms, the central nervous system fascinated her the most.

Professor Levi was not an eloquent teacher, but he was an internationally respected scientist. Tall and robust, he possessed a thunderous voice. His wife, Lidia, used to call him "Levipom" on account of his red hair (*pom* for *pomodoro*, or "tomato"), their daughter Natalia Ginzburg tells us in her autobiographical novel *Family Sayings* (*Lessico famigliare*).[25] Even though Lidia was the only one allowed to use this nickname, Levi's students would secretly call him this, too. He was always absorbed in his own world, totally oblivious to his appearance. According to Rita, "he looked like a writer of the Tolstoy sort, landed in our midst by mistake."[26] His specialty was histology or microscopic anatomy rather than the dissecting table. Born in Trieste to a family of Jewish bankers, he had studied at the universities of Florence and Vienna, where he became fluent in German, which was the preferred language of biologists until the 1930s. He dedicated his career to studying nerve tissue under the microscope. He became head of the Institute of Normal Anatomy in Turin in 1919 and kept this post until he was forced to leave in 1938 because of anti-Jewish laws enacted by Italy's fascist government. Though he took the oath of allegiance to the fascist regime imposed on university professors in 1931, Levi was openly anti-fascist. He refused to hide his hatred for Mussolini and his party, to the alarm of casual listeners who may have shared his opinions in private but preferred to keep silent in public.

In spite of her mentor's idiosyncrasies, Rita was attracted to his exceptional energy and passion for research. He was not related to Rita and yet he reminded her of her father. He was unsparing of himself and his students alike. Like Adamo, he was a dominating presence and had a terrible temper. His tumultuous nature emerges clearly from his daughter's celebrated novel.[27]

Rita was very shy, dressed plainly, and was not particularly interested in courtship. She was seen as a "kind of squid, ready to squirt ink at anybody who would come near her."[28] Nonetheless, she had a few friends who showed a special interest in her, namely Guido Bonnet and Germano Rondolini. She met Guido in her first year and felt attracted to him because he was a long way ahead of her in music; he was constantly whistling a theme from a Beethoven symphony or an aria from Mozart or Schubert. They used to go out for a ride together on his motorbike or take long walks in Valentino Park, exchanging ideas about literature and the arts. Their enriching friendship lasted for a long time, past the Second World War, during which he distinguished himself as an anti-fascist, commonly known as a partisan, siding with the Allies against the Germans. She liked him very much, but, as she observed regretfully in a radio interview many years later, he did not seem to fully appreciate her scientific vocation.

She also became friendly with Germano, whom she met during a class held in the anatomy amphitheater. He introduced himself while she was busy with a dissection. He constantly tossed back his blond hair, revealing his striking blue eyes. He was the son of a medical doctor from a little mountain village near Novara called Villadossola. He started that day a discreet courtship based on courtesy and respect, which persisted beyond their graduation.

In early 1938 he openly declared his love when the anti-Semitic campaign was becoming more and more threatening. He started coming to Rita's house, meeting her mother and siblings in the hope of sharing a life together. However, in October of the same year, a law was passed that adamantly prohibited marriage between Aryan and Jewish people.

When Rita was deprived of her right to practice medicine and dismissed from her academic position at the Institute of Anatomy, she accepted an offer to work in Brussels at the Neurology Institute. While in Belgium, she received a letter from Germano every day. His health, however, unexpectedly began to deteriorate and he was diagnosed with tuberculosis. She was sincerely hoping that his tough mountain spirit would help him recover. Instead he developed an additional complication, a serious kidney infection, which proved to be fatal. As soon as she found out he had returned to his parents' village, she decided to visit him, accompanied by her brother, Gino. Unfortunately, Germano was no longer conscious when they finally met again. While she was away, he had become a convinced anti-fascist, and until the end he expressed his great concern for a possible imminent persecution of Rita's family. His last letter was covered in tears of love and appreciation. When he died, he was only twenty-eight, and left Rita, as a memento of their special bond, a wristwatch that Gino had given him. He knew he no longer needed to measure time.

From the beginning of her second year in medical school, Rita was also blessed with the company of a group of interesting fellow students, some of whom became friends for life.

To overcome her grief and sense of loss after her father died, she spent most of her time at the university, either in the lab or in the library, which was the pride of the Institute of Anatomy. She would spend long hours reading scientific publications that were difficult to obtain. The temperature there would go no higher than about 53 degrees Fahrenheit (12 degrees Celsius), as part of Professor Levi's campaign to discourage students from lingering just to relax; after all, he declared, "a library is not a tavern."[29] It was during this period that she met Rodolfo Amprino, Renato Dulbecco, Salvatore Luria, and Cornelio Fazio.

Rodolfo was younger than Rita, but two years ahead of her. He was considered by Professor Levi to be the most gifted of his students. He had become Levi's intern at seventeen and was twenty when he met Rita. He would frown and shake his head whenever he inspected Rita's slides under the microscope. She could never have imagined how important he would become in her life during the war and the persecution of the Jewish people.

Renato Dulbecco, five years younger than Rita, had also become an intern at the Institute of Anatomy. He was from Imperia in Liguria, where his father worked as an engineer. From the very beginning he proved exceptionally able in every scientific subject, from physics to biology to chemistry, but was notably modest and humble about his abilities. Rita and Renato would exchange precious histological "recipes" with great generosity. She would occasionally speak with him in the library to exchange information about the results of their respective experiments.

She had the same habit with another student, Salvatore Luria (who would later change his name to Salvador Edward Luria after emigrating to the United States in 1940). He was exceptionally intelligent but sometimes impatient and rather "petulant," as Professor Levi used to point out.

Cornelio Fazio was conspicuous, too, for his brilliant academic results, and was in constant competition with Luria. Professor Levi preferred Fazio because of his sensitivity and perceptive nature. During the Second World War, Fazio became a courageous partisan. In spite of the years lost to the war, he would later have a distinguished scientific career.

During the first year of internship, Professor Levi had assigned to Rita and Eugenia, along with other interns, the task of investigating whether the number of neurons in the sensory ganglia—small clumps of nerve cells on either side of each bone of the spinal column—was the same or different in mice from different breeds. The assignment they were engaged in proved to be tedious, time-consuming, approximate, and probably useless, given the fact that the number of cells in the sensory ganglia in a mouse is between ten thousand and twenty thousand. Their thoughts were skeptically echoed by Levi's esteemed colleague Tullio Terni, then professor of anatomy at the University of Padua, on one of his frequent visits to Turin. He wittily compared their task of counting the nerve cells of mice to counting the leaves of the two plane trees outside the laboratory window.

Unheard by Professor Levi, Terni suggested that this would be just as valuable since he also rather doubted the counts could be accurate, regardless of how carefully they had been done. However, deep down, the bizarre request made by Levi, who proved to be so much ahead of his time, had a significant purpose: to determine whether the number of cells in clearly identifiable nerve groupings is fixed or instead subject to fluctuations due to environmental factors. Neither Rita nor Eugenia yielded to the easy temptation to which so many interns had succumbed: making up their figures. Even though they were novices who did not fully grasp the relevance of such painstaking research, they delivered counts that actually confirmed Levi's forecasts and he generously acknowledged these students' contribution in an important treatise on histology. Rita passed her first year's exams with honors, along with Eugenia.

Rita started the new term with renewed commitment. However, her enthusiasm did not last very long because she was assigned a project that soon turned out to be even more arduous, if not impossible. She was supposed to determine how the convolutions, or folds, of the human brain were formed before birth. The assigned research topic differed this time from Eugenia's; she was more fortunate in being asked to conduct similar research on calf fetuses. These were available in large quantities at the slaughterhouse and the research could easily be carried out by means of common histological techniques. Rita's task, however, posed a real predicament.

In the early 1930s, human fetuses could hardly be procured for experimental purposes. In those days abortion in Italy was illegal; therefore, hospitals could not supply Rita with any specimens, and the very few doctors and midwives who performed these clandestine operations were unwilling to risk cooperation in secret. Only an occasional fetus, after a spontaneous or medically necessary abortion, could be obtained, usually several days after the miscarriage and in poorly preserved condition.

Rita, however, was determined not to surrender. She had asked the caretaker of Ospedale Maggiore, the main hospital in Turin, to get her a human fetus from an early stage and, after paying him some *lire*, she got instead, in a bundle of newspapers, a stillborn child who had been dead for more than three days. The students' counselor helped Rita to dissect the brain, even though fully developed, but reprimanded her for her reckless behavior. In his opinion, by carrying a dead child wrapped in a newspaper in her arms on public transport, she risked ending up in jail. Moreover, the counselor was convinced that Rita should never have accepted such a dangerous and unrewarding task from Professor Levi. All the same, he patiently showed her that the convolutions had already been fully formed. The tiny brain fell apart right away under the surgical scalpel, preventing Rita from any histological examination.

So, while Eugenia's research proceeded at full steam, Rita began to lose faith in herself, thinking she had no future as a laboratory scientist. The outspoken Levi was disappointed to the point of calling her histologic preparations *delle grandi porcherie*,[30] "real trash." She thought from his belittling remarks that he considered her inept in her academic research.

As fate would have it, Rita suddenly had to undergo an emergency operation for a severe case of kidney stones. She was whisked off to a clinic, where she stayed for a month and was thus spared continuing with the convolution project she dreaded. She was also surprised to receive several uplifting visits from Professor Levi, who cared deeply about his students, especially if they became ill.[31]

Thanks to her sudden illness, a gratifying master-disciple relationship started to develop, based on reciprocal esteem and affection, that lasted for over thirty years, until Levi's death. From the time Rita landed in the clinic, Professor Giuseppe Levi became her true mentor, and when she went back to class, she was given a new assignment that restored her passion for research and shaped her future career.

She was requested, along with Eugenia, to find out the roles that three types of tissue (the connective, muscular, and epithelial) played in forming the weblike network of fibers that supported them in the brain stem.[32] To their great satisfaction, they both managed to prove for the first time that the formation of reticular fibers was not a property of connective tissue alone, but of muscular and epithelial tissues as well. Rita had started developing a certain ability in applying the silver impregnation technique on nerve tissues, according to the so-called Golgi method.

Camillo Golgi was an Italian histologist who had invented the method of chrome silver impregnation, which makes nerve cells stand out in the smallest detail: black, against the golden background of surrounding tissues. Around 1870 Golgi was working as a doctor at the hospice for terminal patients Pia Casa degli Incurabili at Abbiategrasso, near Pavia, in Lombardy. He got permission to conduct research as well, but had no resources to do so. He improvised a lab in the rudimentary kitchen of the building, providing it with a microscope and a few other instruments. After many attempts with a host of different solutions, he found the right one for the purpose of highlighting the shape of the cells of the nervous system.

Yet it would have been impossible to identify the roughly one hundred billion nerve cells that usually constitute any single human brain had Santiago Ramón y Cajal—great histologist and founder of the science of neurology—not opted to analyze the nervous system at an early stage of embryonic development, when it consisted of a few hundred cells. The chick embryo was the specimen he preferred—and it is still the preferred species— because its brain is identical to the basic unit of the nervous system of all vertebrates including man and is easily available.[33]

Golgi and Ramón y Cajal jointly received the Nobel Prize in 1906. Ramón y Cajal was rewarded for his neuron theory, which proved to be the first theory that identified the cellular makeup of the nervous system. It was unfortunate, however, that his illustrious colleague Golgi never accepted Ramón y Cajal's theory—indeed, vehemently opposed it on the grounds that, according to him, nerve impulses traveled uninterrupted through the fibrous systems. His reticular theory was proven incorrect in the first two decades of the twentieth century, but had delayed the advance of scientific knowledge in the field. Ramón y Cajal had instead followed his visionary intuition that every cell was and is an independent unit and that the ends of its fibers are not physically connected. The spaces between the cells were hardly visible under the microscope, but he firmly believed in this assumption even before more advanced tools fully confirmed his theory.

Professor Levi looked on Ramón y Cajal as his invaluable scientific point of reference and became a pioneer in Italy of in vitro studies of cultured cells. He realized right away that they provided a unique opportunity for investigating the development of the brain cells while controlling their environment.

Adopting the silver-impregnation technique Rita had become familiar with, Rita and Eugenia proved for the first time that the formation of reticular fibers, which can be revealed by a particular argentic staining, is not a property of connective tissues alone, but also of muscular and epithelial tissues.[34] Until then, it had been believed that collagen reticular fibers namely the fibers that make up the weft that supports the complex of tissues of which they are a part, were produced by special cells present in great numbers in bone, cartilage, and subcutaneous tissues alone.

This research was the basis for Rita and Eugenia's doctoral thesis, which earned them top honors when they received their MD degrees in 1936. As a reward, Professor Levi invited Rita and Eugenia to an international anatomy conference in Copenhagen, Denmark.

This successful assignment induced Rita to share Levi's life mission: the study of nerve cells in vitro, which became the guiding principle of all her future research, culminating in the discovery of nerve growth factor.

Chapter Four

THE RISE OF FASCISM AND THE ANTI-SEMITIC LAWS

Premonitions of trouble to come had been there since Rita was in high school. Italy had suffered severe economic depression after the First World War, which caused widespread social discontentment to the point where the country became politically unstable.

Inflation was rampant, and by 1920 a series of workers' strikes and violent demonstrations were destabilizing the country. Many Italians, especially of the upper and middle classes, were afraid that socialists and communists, who supported the workers' revolt, might take their property away; the Bolshevik Revolution in 1917 was hardly a reassuring precedent. They longed for "strong government." The solution seemed to lie in the hands of an emerging political figure: Benito Mussolini.

In his youth he was an active socialist and editor of *Avanti!*, the official Socialist Party newspaper. He maintained that workers would have a better chance to gain power if they were consolidated, like individual stalks of wheat joined in sturdy bundles, or *fasces*, a political symbol since ancient Roman times. In 1919 he founded a party called Fasci di Combattimento, an elite revolutionary movement that in 1921 became the Partito Nazionale Fascista, a national corporatist movement, supposedly class-free and "collective." His party included numerous Jews who had distinguished themselves in various fields. He believed they should be fully integrated into his party and not exiled to the fringes of the nation. In *Il Popolo d'Italia*, a newspaper he directly controlled, Mussolini stated: "Italy knows no anti-Semitism and we are convinced she shall never know it."

Mussolini did not view the Jews with either sympathy or antagonism; he recognized that the Jews were successful and clever, especially in the financial and economic fields, and he held them in high esteem.[35] In an article in the same paper, he affirmed: "In Italy we make absolutely no difference between Jews and non-Jews, in every field, religion, politics, the army, the economy . . . Italian Jews have their new Zion right here, in our beautiful land, which many of them have defended heroically with their blood."

His party also accommodated a paramilitary voluntary group, the Camicie Nere, or "Black Shirts." Its members were identified by their black uniforms and their personal loyalty to Mussolini, swearing an oath to that effect. Their methods became harsher as Mussolini's power grew, and they were not afraid to use intimidation and brute force against his opponents. In 1922, after what was to all intents and purposes a coup spearheaded by the famous March on Rome, King Victor Emmanuel III asked Mussolini to form a government.

In June 1924, Giacomo Matteotti, iconic leader of the Unitary Socialist Party, disappeared. Fascist-leaning newspapers suggested he had fled the country, but eyewitnesses came forward who had seen him seized off the street in Rome by five people who forced him into a car, which drove off at full speed in the direction of Ponte Milvio. The murder of Matteotti was the first overt act of government-sponsored violence since Mussolini had come to power and the backlash very nearly toppled him. He managed, however, to see off a divided opposition, which included members of his own party, and on January 3, 1925, he took sole control of the government, while the king remained on the throne as a figurehead, becoming increasingly irrelevant. Mussolini's totalitarian policy worked to strengthen his power at its roots. It was especially effective with the middle classes, who sought in his false ideals a justification for their ineptitude. His demagogy appealed increasingly to the glorious race of Italians, legitimate heirs of the Imperial Rome of the Caesars, history's greatest power. Thanks to this stratagem, Mussolini was exalted as a mass idol, soon assuming the title of Il Duce, or "The Leader."

In 1933 the government in Germany fell into the hands of Adolf Hitler, the founder of Nazism, or German fascism. Like Mussolini, Hitler, too, declared himself Führer—the equivalent of Duce—and became a mass idol. His formula to cement his political ascendancy involved harping on the innate superiority of the German race, and the supremacy of Aryans in general. As a consequence, the establishment of the Third Reich required the unconditional subjugation and eventually extermination of all inferior races, beginning with the Jews and the Roma, and including even mentally or physically "defective" Germans. The year 1933 marked the beginning of the systematic persecution of Jews in Germany.[36]

Mussolini's dictatorship, which lasted until 1945, brought with it the disbanding of opposition parties and parliamentary minorities, the suppression of the free press, and the repression of most forms of independent cultural life, all under the guise of legitimate legal measures. Italy was deprived of a number of outstanding political and cultural personalities because many of its intellectuals opted for self-exile, often in clandestine fashion. Great numbers emigrated to France, among whom was Professor Levi's future son-in-law, Leone Ginzburg, who joined the anti-fascist movement Giustizia e Libertà ("Justice and Freedom") in Paris while constantly keeping in touch with developments in his own country, and returning to Turin in 1932 to found a new branch of the movement.[37] Dissidents who chose to stay in Italy and refused to adhere to the fascist regime were imprisoned or confined to house arrest, unless they opted for a clandestine life.

Rita saw the first signs of fascist repression in action in March 1934 with the arrest of Sion Segre, her fellow student. He was a follower of Carlo and Nello Rosselli's chapter of Giustizia e Libertà (the two brothers would be murdered in Normandy in

1937 by order of Mussolini and Count Ciano, his son-in-law). Along with Leone Ginzburg, Segre was caught by the police at the Swiss border with a suitcase full of anti-fascist pamphlets.[38] They were both condemned: Ginzburg to four years in jail and Segre to three. After a few months, however, Segre managed to go back to working at the lab, thanks to being granted two years' probation. Ginzburg and Segre's companion, Mario Levi, son of Rita's mentor, managed to escape into Switzerland by diving into a river and swimming across, in spite of the freezing temperature.[39] Many of the others arrested at this time were not only opponents of the Fascist Party, but were also Jews, as established in detail by Renzo De Felice, one of the most eminent twentieth-century Italian historians, who provided the names: Sion Segre, Attilio Segre, Giuliana Segre, Marco Segre, Leo Levi, Riccardo Levi, Carlo Levi, Gino Levi, Carlo Vercelli, and Leone Ginzburg.[40]

Carlo Levi, a distinguished doctor, writer, and painter from Turin, spent his two years of internal exile in a remote village for his anti-fascist clandestine activity along with Leone Ginzburg. Levi's novel *Christ Stopped at Eboli* centers on his experience among the peasants of Lucania (now Basilicata), one of the poorest and most backward regions of the impoverished Italian south. He felt the duty to side with these disinherited people, abandoned by the central government. Their world, as noted by Italo Calvino, was kept outside of history, yet within it, Carlo Levi paradoxically saw an extraordinary potential.

In March 1934 Professor Giuseppe Levi was arrested, and, not knowing that his son Mario had successfully reached

Switzerland at the price of serious pneumonia, claimed to be the only one responsible for the conspiracy. Luckily enough, the Italian fascist policeman who arrested him did not believe him and, apparently thanks to Professor Levi's sense of humor, set him free after two weeks, thinking him a harmless old madman. Levi's other son, Gino, however, was kept in jail for two more months on suspicion of being an anti-fascist agitator. Though Professor Levi never missed an occasion to speak openly and passionately against the regime, he was officially a fascist himself, at least insofar as he had been forced reluctantly to swear an oath of loyalty to the regime in order not to jeopardize his position at the university. In spite of this, he was later forced to resign in 1938 when the racial laws were enforced.

In pre-fascist Italian political life, and even during the early years of fascism, there was little anti-Semitic tradition or racism; on the contrary, despite the slandering efforts of certain groups and publications harping on a few notorious clichés and popular legends, Italian Jews were highly respected in many cities in northern Italy.[41] Since the Risorgimento, the Zionist movement for the reconstruction of a country for the Jews had found support in Italy. Camillo Benso, Count of Cavour, Italy's first prime minister, was an early supporter of what finally became the state of Israel in 1947.

During the early years of fascism, Mussolini was considered almost a champion of Judaism, no doubt for opportunistic reasons. In fact, membership was open to Jews, many of whom financed the party. Mussolini had often histrionically stated:

"The Jews have lived in Rome since the days of the Kings . . . and shall remain undisturbed."

After Hitler took over the Chancellery and the Nazi party published its infamous proclamation about the Jews in 1933, Mussolini initially declared that fascism was disassociating itself from Nazism, to the point where he intervened on behalf of three thousand German Jews by welcoming them to Italy. At their first meeting on June 16, 1934, at the Palazzo Ferro Fini hotel in Venice, Mussolini suggested to Hitler that the Nazi anti-Semitic campaign was a political mistake. Mussolini later dramatically declared, "Thirty centuries of history allow us to gaze with sovereign disdain at some of the doctrines coming from behind the Alps, propagated by the progeny of people who did not know how to write documents about their own lives at a time when Rome had Caesar, Virgil, and Augustus."

By the mid-thirties, thousands of Jews had fled the threat of Nazism. Many moved into Italy or Italian-controlled territories, seeing them as safe havens. Il Duce himself had a Jewish mistress, Margherita Sarfatti—the editor of the fascist magazine *Gerarchia*—who played a very important role in his policy-making from 1922 until 1938, when Mussolini unfortunately bowed to German pressure, with tragic consequences.

Renzo De Felice, an important Italian historian who specialized in the fascist era, maintained, in his monumental eight-volume biography *Mussolini* and in *The Jews in Fascist Italy: A History*, that Il Duce promoted anti-Semitism in Italy as a way to curry favor with Hitler:

Upon the altar of his alliance with Hitler, Mussolini sacrificed the Italian Jews without second thought, even though he did not really believe in their "guilt"; thus committing a crime more monstrous even than that committed by the Nazis, who at least did believe in the "guilt" of the Jews: in the same way that of his own accord he sacrificed the Jews to Hitler, had he been the ally of Stalin he would have sacrificed something else. Hitler's ally became a racist and Anti-Semite.[42]

In 1936 Italy's conquest of Ethiopia and the expansion of what the regime regarded as Italy's "colonial empire" brought the question of race to the forefront as never before. Mussolini allowed himself to be influenced by the pseudo-scientific writings of Julius Evola, eventually encapsulated in *Sintesi della dottrina della razza* (*Synthesis of the Doctrine of Race*), in which the author promotes the Aryo-Romans as the "central guiding race," a spiritual race. Such doctrines were precisely what Mussolini needed. They allowed him to approach issues similar to those obsessing Germany, and therefore align himself while maintaining a certain independence of attitude by introducing a "spiritual" orientation that he thought missing from the cruder German racism. More precisely, the theory of an Aryo-Roman race could mythically integrate the general ethos of fascism, and create a basis for Mussolini's plan to transform and uplift the average Italian from "a race of slaves" to a "race of lords" and noble conquerors. Such a race would be both new and ancient, the embodiment of the principle *mens sana in corpore sano* ("a healthy mind in a healthy body"), giving birth to no less than the "fascist man."

Amid the first signs of these events and in spite of an increase in propagandistic, racist attacks on Jews, Rita was just in time to graduate from medical school in 1936. By then, Mussolini had appointed his son-in-law Galeazzo Ciano as Minister of Foreign Affairs. The change of command at Palazzo Chigi had deep repercussions insofar as Ciano bore enormous responsibility for having taken Italy down the road to a disastrous alliance with Hitler.

During the next two years, Jews were accused first sporadically and then more frequently in the Italian press. The notoriously anti-Semitic newspapers, such as *Il Tevere* and *Il Regime Fascista*, as well as more liberal and neutral ones, including *La Stampa*, became increasingly aligned with Nazi Germany and its hatred for the Jewish race. According to Rita, the monster of anti-Semitism, all the more menacing for being invisible and yet ever present, "had to come out of its lair."[43]

The Second Coming, by one of her favorite poets, William Butler Yeats, comes inevitably to mind:

> *The darkness drops again but now I know*
> *That twenty centuries of stony sleep*
> *Were vexed to nightmare by a rocking cradle,*
> *And what rough beast, its hour come round at last,*
> *Slouches towards Bethlehem to be born?*[44]

During her childhood and adolescence, Rita sometimes had nightmares after hearing from her father all the tribulations suffered by the Jews and the restrictions placed on Jewish people in several parts of Italy, including the Republic of Venice, where Jews since 1516 were confined to an area called the Ghetto (which subsequently lent its name to many other such places) until the Napoleonic armies invaded northern Italy. Motivated by a new spirit pervading Europe, Napoleon promoted Jewish integration into society, although it was not until 1868, two years before the final unification of Italy, and thanks to Victor Emmanuel II, that Piedmont adopted a law conferring the same rights on all citizens regardless of religion. For a long time after this legal turning point, Italian Jews felt welcome and thoroughly integrated.

Gradually Il Duce, maneuvering to align himself with Germany while shrewdly safeguarding his "innocence," initiated a systematic propaganda campaign in the press to "educate" or rather manipulate public opinion.

In response to these unjust attacks, Rita, suddenly and for the first time, felt proud of being Jewish, nurturing a deep bond with all the victims of the infamous campaign unleashed by the fascist party because they were innocent of the crimes of which they had been accused and regrettably unable to defend themselves.

Nonetheless, the idea of state-sponsored anti-Semitism was far removed from Mussolini's mind until 1937. His true aspiration even at that point was not to persecute, still less exterminate the Jews. He intended to find a territorial solution outside of

Europe, in East Africa, possibly in the Horn of Africa or Upper Juba, where Jews might settle and flourish. This high-handed project even involved contact at some point with US President Franklin D. Roosevelt, but Mussolini eventually relinquished the potential role of deus ex machina. His excuse was that the issue had ceased being strictly Italian and had acquired a wider European dimension.

On July 14, 1938, the *Manifesto of Race*—clearly conceived, if not actually written, by Mussolini himself, and in blatant contradiction with his previous convictions—appeared in most Italian newspapers. It was signed by ten "scientists" of no great distinction and their assistants, with the purpose of creating an ideological and scientific platform for state-sponsored anti-Semitism. It declared that Jews did not belong to the Italian race because "of the Semites who in the course of centuries have landed on the sacred soil of our Fatherland, nothing on the whole has remained."[45] The *Manifesto* remains one of the worst episodes of the fascist period from a scientific, political, and moral point of view. In the meantime, in Germany, in the aftermath of Kristallnacht, German citizens were virtually authorized to perpetrate an unhindered persecution, even murder, of Jews.

In November of the same year, following the dictates of Germany, the promulgation of the racial laws in Italy enforced a stage of irreversible discrimination. Belonging to "the Italian race" became the essential prerequisite to holding public positions. From that moment on, any Jew could be legally fired on that pretext alone. No tolerance or compassion was allowed. The government passed a number of measures that prevented Jews from leading a normal life. They could not, for example, marry non-Jews, as specified in the Royal Decree dated November 17, 1938:

ARTICLE 1

The marriage of an Italian citizen of the Aryan race with a person belonging to another race is prohibited. A marriage celebrated despite such prohibition is invalid.

ARTICLE 8

a) Those born of parents who are both of the Jewish race, even if belonging to religions different from the Jewish religion, are considered of the Jewish race.
b) Those born of parents of which one is of the Jewish race and the other of foreign nationality, are considered of the Jewish race . . .

ARTICLE 9

Belonging to the Jewish race must be declared and entered in the records of Registrar of births, deaths and marriages and the bureau of statistics.

This specific decree has been considered the Magna Carta of Italian racism. It proved to be a law full of contradictions and went far beyond the decisions of the Grand Council. Mussolini thought that his new hybrid formula based on the principle of "discrimination, not persecution" would be accepted, thanks to the propaganda bombardment he had encouraged. Instead, it was rejected by the overwhelming majority of Italians, who quickly grasped that to discriminate meant either to fail to solve the problem or to persecute. Moreover, because of the alliance with Germany, Mussolini quickly found himself trapped in a dead end.[46]

As a consequence, citizens of "the Jewish race" were banned from all professions and in practice barred from virtually all employment: They were excluded from the management of businesses, properties, and possessions, and were forbidden to attend schools of any kind.[47] Many young people were forced to abandon their studies, such as Bruno Zevi, a future professor of architecture. He moved first to England and then to the United States, where he graduated from the Harvard Graduate School of Design, under the directorship of another exile, Walter Gropius. He returned to Italy only after the fall of fascism in 1945.

All Jewish professors, scientists, and intellectuals were barred from the country's universities. The only exception was made for students, including foreigners, already matriculated at the universities, who were allowed to complete the courses they had already begun.[48] Thus, Rita was able to complete her postgraduate studies. According to an August 1938 compulsory census, doctors in Turin who were Jewish numbered 203 out of 1,463, engineers 79 out of 960, accountants 34 out of 180, industrial accountants 14 out of 332, notaries 9 out of 108, and lawyers 124 out of 962.[49]

At this stage Mussolini intended to keep the population

of Jews in Italy, about forty-five thousand, in the proportion of one for every one thousand inhabitants. The participation of the Jewish minority in the total life of the state, in his words, "must and shall be adjusted in this proportion." To monitor this bizarre formula, the census had to be continually updated, even during the war years, from 1941 to 1943.

The national policy of hatred had triumphed, aligning Italy with Hitler's Nazi regime, which would be responsible in the end for the genocide of over five million Jews and millions of other innocent victims such as communists, socialists, Jehovah's Witnesses, homosexuals—in other words, all the perceived enemies of the Reich.

At that time, Rita was completely engaged in exciting research on the spontaneous activity of chick embryos from the very first days of their development, which combined her colleague Fabio Visentini's expertise in neurophysiology with her own in neurology. She was studying the differentiation of the neuron centers by examining sections of embryos under the microscope following the impregnation technique she had learned so well at the university from the examples of Camillo Golgi and Santiago Ramón y Cajal, and had herself refined. Their successful joint analysis brought together results from Turin's Clinic for Nervous and Mental Diseases, where Visentini was working, and her own university, resulting in an insightful article that was rejected because Italian scientific journals were not authorized to publish articles by Jews. However, it was published a year later by a prestigious Swiss magazine noted for its innovative content.

On the basis of a racial law proclaimed on October 16, 1938, Rita found herself unemployed. She had fought against the paternalistic mentality prevailing at the time, painfully asserted her rights with her father, studied so hard to be admitted to the university, and completed complex medical studies with the highest marks. She had only just started to work and be financially independent when she was forced to leave, losing her job overnight after having proven she was one of the best in her department. Being "of Jewish race," she was suspended from any academic work and was not allowed to teach or accept any other position. Government measures of increasing severity gradually stripped her, as they did all Jews, of the right to participate in any activity in the country.

Il Duce's latest alarming decisions, endorsed on October 6, 1938, by the Grand Council, met with only a token resistance from King Victor Emmanuel III and the Holy See, reluctant to jeopardize the delicate equilibrium between church and state. One of the very few to speak out was national hero and aviator Italo Balbo, who was also the only leading fascist to challenge Mussolini's alliance with Nazi Germany.

Hitler was showing no signs of adopting a more conciliatory policy. After annexing Austria, the Führer proceeded to invade Czechoslovakia, immediately imitated by Il Duce, who annexed Albania.

Rita now decided that the safest thing to do was to emigrate. She could disappear from the Italian scene by accepting an invitation to work in Belgium, at a neurological institute in Brussels. The offer was enticing since her sister Nina, her husband, and their three children had already decided to escape the mounting terrors of Turin and were now living in Brussels. Moreover, Professor Levi had decided to continue his scientific activity at the university in the Belgian city of Liège, where Rita was able to visit him once a week. He had set up a tissue culture center there and his energy was at its peak; he was even embarking on new research on the muscular system.

Rita lived in Brussels for almost ten months, from March to December 1939. Belgians then lived in constant fear of a German invasion, with painful memories of the First World War still very much alive. While Rita was in Stockholm at an international conference that year, she heard the alarming news of Hitler's invasion of Poland.

The response from the West was immediate: France and Britain declared war on Germany. The Second World War had begun. Now, with Germany on the offensive, even Belgium felt unsafe, so Rita, along with Nina and her family, decided to drive across France back to Turin.

On Christmas Eve, 1938, Mussolini had publicly declared his country would not go to war. Many Italian Jews living elsewhere were thus persuaded that Italy might be a safer haven and returned home. Their naive hopes were dashed only five months later when Italy formed a military and political alliance with Germany, called the "Pact of Steel." Known formally as the Pact of Friendship and Alliance, it was signed on May 22, 1939, by both foreign ministers, Galeazzo Ciano of Italy and Joachim von Ribbentrop of Germany. The two countries, who had been enemies in the First World War, came together against the allied forces of France, Britain, and later, the United States.

The situation of the Jews of Italy had taken a radical turn for the worse. It was even suggested that they were in some way responsible for the outbreak of the war. This was clearly an attempt to exonerate fascism and the Axis powers—Germany, Italy, and Japan, plus a few other countries—from any responsibility in the matter.

Most Jews had been caught completely off guard by the enactment of the first anti-Semitic laws, which provoked a wave of indignation but certainly no corrective measures. Persecution was so far removed from the mentality, history, and traditions of Italy, so unwarranted from every point of view, that most Jews thought it merely a foreign policy initiative. Almost no one made the connection between the Pact of Steel and the imminent turn toward anti-Semitism in Mussolini, who, unlike other European statesmen, had honorably welcomed so many refugees from other countries. Jews living in Italy were Italians to the core— by birth, culturally, educationally, and in a way, doubly Italian, because to them Italy meant emancipation and civic equality attained only a few decades before.[50] The persecution was not only a material fact, but primarily a moral issue. Among the Jews, disbelief and disoriented amazement gave way to painful realization as larger sections of the Italian people accustomed themselves to the persecution, allowing their sensitivities to be blunted by the routine of everyday life, by the fear of having problems with the regime, and even, among the educated classes, by the desire for positions vacated by Jews.[51] Jewish writers such as Italo Svevo and Alberto Moravia, whose books were banned during the fascist regime, were vilified as being morally, perhaps physically, sick.

Psychoanalysis was demonized as an ally of Judaism; Austrian neurologist Sigmund Freud was belittled as a Jew judging others by the standards of his own race. Giorgio Bassani, a writer from a prosperous Jewish family of Ferrara, became a clandestine political activist, living under the assumed name of Giacomo Marchi. After being briefly arrested, he was fortunate enough to be released, and he documented in many of his novels, notably his masterpiece *The Garden of the Finzi-Continis*, the painful marginalization of Jews and homosexuals during fascism. Real, conscious opposition to the persecution remained in most cases confined to pockets of the Italian population: simple, honest people; morally aware Catholics; and anti-fascists.

The hope, or rather the illusion, of finding solidarity and understanding was at this point almost impossible to entertain.

Chapter Five

A LAB IN THE BEDROOM

In 1938, Rita had lost her academic position for which she had worked so hard. She was forced to ask herself a very painful question: Where was she now in life?

She had no idea. For her, as for all Italian Jews, the years that followed, up to the fall of fascism, were to be years of long and difficult adaptation to their new condition as second-class citizens.[52] There was no way to counter all the false accusations that appeared in the press, and above all, little to be done about the unjust laws that had been passed, reluctantly endorsed even by the Catholic Church, whose latent anti-Semitism was acutely analyzed by Antonio Gramsci in the notebooks he kept during his imprisonment at the hands of Mussolini's fascist regime.[53]

Starting a family was also out of the question for Rita. Though this was not her priority, she could not marry any of her potential suitors even if she wanted to, because it was illegal. While her Aryan colleagues would inevitably advance their careers, she had been shunned like a criminal. She felt that she had no future—but at least she retained the privilege of still being alive and able to carry on thinking and cultivating her inner resources.

During this early period of brooding, she decided to try to practice medicine clandestinely. The people she knew who had been in her care at the university clinic were determined to ignore the new laws and were grateful to count on her voluntary work as a doctor. However, since only non-Jewish physicians could prescribe drugs, it became increasingly difficult and risky to be of help. In spite of her desire to assist at least the people she knew and cared for, she first reduced and then abandoned her medical practice.

In the spring of 1940, the first phase of the Second World War was marked by the Führer's rapid occupation of Denmark, Norway, the Netherlands, Belgium, Luxembourg, and France. Convinced of Germany's imminent total victory, Il Duce, who had been waiting to see which way the wind blew, decided at the last moment to honor the Pact of Steel ("a few thousand dead will be worth a seat at the peace table"). Four days before the Germans entered Paris, Mussolini declared war against France and Great Britain. What was supposed to be a *blitzkrieg*, or lightning war, against the latter nation instead stalled beyond expectation. Beset by uninterrupted German air raids on London, Coventry, and other cities, literally pulverizing roads and harbors, England put up a desperate resistance.

It was on June 10, 1940, in Rome's Piazza Venezia, in

front of an immense, oblivious, cheering crowd, that Mussolini informed the Italians of his irrevocable decision to enter the war. The next day, France was attacked from the southeast, and Italy, in the so-called Battle of the Alps, promptly lost two thousand soldiers because the Italian troops were utterly unready for combat; similar tragic consequences would also ensue on the African and Greek fronts. Il Duce's sudden invasion of Greece, predicted to be an "easy stroll," proved disastrous. The Italian fleet suffered severe losses in the Mediterranean, while during the North African Campaign, the Italians had difficulty defending their garrisons against attack from the British desert army.

By the fall of 1940, Rita had become a sort of hermit. Her employment was gone, and after Germano's death, the love of her life was gone as well. She had been cruelly robbed of her vocation and she could not hope for a sudden reversal of fate. What possible goal could she aim at now? What did she have to live for? She was in danger of stagnating, losing all energy, and succumbing to inertia when she received an unexpected visit from her former colleague Rodolfo Amprino on his return from the United States.

Finding her depressed, restless, and unmotivated, he decided to be provocative, quizzing her about her projects. She had none, she admitted, having been forced to suspend her recent successful experiment with Dr. Visentini combining her studies on the growth of nerve cells with his specialty in electrophysiology. Rodolfo strongly suggested she should abandon idle speculations or impossible hopes and react by giving herself a focus, a purpose. He reminded her that Santiago Ramón y Cajal, in the middle of the nineteenth century in a poorly equipped institute in Valencia, Spain—then a very sleepy town—had managed to become the pioneer of modern neuroscience with his original investigations on the brain, creating the basis of what we know about the nervous system of vertebrates.[54]

She was surprised about Rodolfo's interest in her, since their meetings at the Anatomy Institute eight years earlier had been very short and limited to occasional exchanges of information. Rodolfo did not approve of the new anti-Semitic laws in Italy and had to visit Rita in secret for both of their sakes. His first statement was: "One does not lose heart in the face of the first difficulties."

Their fortuitous meeting proved to be a heaven-sent turning point. Suddenly her deep interest in science and letters resurfaced. She felt as if she were in front of Ulysses, who, in the twenty-sixth canto of Dante's *Inferno*, encourages his companions to continue their journey, past the pillars of Hercules, to pursue "virtue and knowledge" and inevitably discover new lands:

Fatti non foste a viver come bruti,
ma per seguir virtute e canoscenza.
(You were not made to live like beasts, but men,
to follow virtue and strive for knowledge.)[55]

Without realizing it, Rodolfo had encouraged Rita to

undertake a perilous journey into the unexplored territories of the brain, delving into the nervous system and its labyrinthine network of billions of cells. This unexpected positive interaction opened up vital possibilities for her.

Inspired by this courageous idea of starting a home laboratory, she decided to resume her research. This would surely help her to overcome her wistful daydreaming and brooding. She talked to her mother and siblings, and they unanimously approved of her challenging project. Her mother was ready to make any sacrifice, provided Rita did not leave Turin again. Moreover, Gino and Paola were confident that Nazi-fascism would be defeated at some point and did not consider the option of moving to the United States, as did Rita's old classmate Salvador Luria, or to Argentina, as did her cousin Eugenia de Lustig and many others, such as Mussolini's former lover Margherita Sarfatti. And ultimately, why *should* she have to suffer so much for being what she was? Why could she not give herself a second chance, even without leaving the country?

She tidied up her little bedroom and turned it into a scientific lab, despite the fact that the space for her new adventure was very limited, since one third of the room was taken up by her single bed. Her solitary activity in what was not unlike a convent cell proved to be therapeutic and uplifting from the very start. She decided she could remain invisible to the world at large for the time being, but still feel alive in a room of her own.

She was able to get chicken eggs from local farmers as they assumed they were for feeding her family. At that time all she wanted was to experiment on chicken embryos which were easy to raise in her home laboratory.

It was not as easy to find the instruments she needed. She limited herself to essentials: two incubators (which could be replaced by thermostats) to seal the embryos in paraffin; a microtome, essential to cut thin slices of tissue for microscopic examination and silver-stain them; two microscopes, including one with a camera; and a few micro scissors she obtained from an eye doctor, together with miniature surgical instruments that she was able to get from a watchmaker without arousing suspicion. She used a fine-grained grindstone to sharpen common sewing needles into tiny scalpels. Her brother, Gino, built her a glass thermo-regulated box with two circular openings through which she could insert her arms and operate on the embryos under the microscope. Her whole family lined up behind her new endeavor.

All through the winter of 1940 and spring of 1941, she worked with intensity and conviction. Would anyone notice her at all in her confinement? Would she be regarded as a local eccentric? On the other hand, she wondered, if Ramón y Cajal, with his exceptional intuition, had "dared foray into that jungle," why should she not venture along the path he had opened for her?[56] She had reached a point where she actually experienced a secret forbidden pleasure at working while hidden under prohibitive conditions. Working around the racial laws made her challenge even more exciting. All she wanted at that time was to understand the factors that regulate nerve fiber growth in the nervous system and carry out some bold new experiments, performing microsurgery on chick embryos and applying silver stain to their nervous tissue.

When Hitler, with the participation of Italy, invaded Stalin's Russia in June of 1941, declaring that it would be "wiped off the map in eight weeks," Rita feared Professor Levi had been captured by the Nazis, since he had refused to leave Belgium after the German occupation. She became very worried, but by the end of the summer, he miraculously managed to reach Turin, after enduring hunger and solitude in Liège for two years and undergoing a very risky trip through Germany. He showed up at her door emaciated, under the fake identity of Giuseppe Lovisatto.[57] In due course he would leave his whole scientific library to the Belgian university as a token of gratitude for offering him work after he had lost his position in Turin.[58]

Levi joyfully accepted an invitation to join Rita in the new research project in her humble improvised laboratory, à la Robinson Crusoe. Teacher and pupil would come together from morning to evening and work indefatigably for a whole year until the Allies' heavy bombing forced them to leave town. Their main objective was to understand the role of the intrinsic, genetic factors vis-à-vis the extrinsic or environmental ones in the differentiation of the nervous centers.

Rita's decision to team up with Levi again gave her a further sense of direction and stability. She felt blessed by the fact that under these unprecedented conditions, the illustrious professor had agreed to collaborate with her on her project, so that she suddenly found herself working with an authority in the field as her only assistant and private mentor. Moreover, in moments of discouragement, he would support her like a particularly caring father figure. The only issue was his great corporeal mass and meager agility, which threatened to destroy the entire carefully laid out histological section with a mere swipe of his large hands each time he moved, as she wittily pointed out later in her autobiography.[59]

Outside, on the streets, anti-Semitic graffiti and posters pasted all over the walls of Turin threatened torture and death for the Jews, but inside her tiny room Rita persisted in her research, which absorbed all of her energies. Most of the time she was observing and recording the patterns of nerve growth in developing embryos, and often she would make detailed drawings of the neural material.

She was always trying to compare notes, to expand her horizons by reading voraciously and extensively to inform her own work with the findings of others, essential to the progress of any scientific research. She had a real epiphany—or rather, "a conversion," to quote her verbatim—when traveling on a livestock train being used for daily transport at that time, with no seats, regular doors, or windows. Reading an article Professor Levi had given her two years earlier, she was sitting on the floor, her legs dangling in the open air, glancing up at the spectacular views offered by the wide-open door. Her close friend Guido kept vigil beside her, whistling an aria from Mozart, as usual. The train progressed very slowly through the countryside, allowing her to see the fields in their summer glory and smell the hay in the air. The article, "The effects of wing bud extirpation on the development of the central nervous system in chick embryos," published in 1934 in *The Journal of Experimental Zoology*, had been written by professor Viktor Hamburger, a pupil of Hans Spemann, the biologist who had been awarded the Nobel Prize in 1935.

Hamburger was a German-born scientist working in the United States and, like Rita, was Jewish. He had accepted a research position at Washington University in St. Louis, Missouri, and decided to stay on after the Nazis took over Germany in 1933. By 1940 he had become head of the university's zoology department. He, too, was investigating the development of the nervous system in chicken embryos. With rigorous analysis he had observed that the ablation of chick embryo limb buds affected the sensory and motor neurons responsible for their innervation.

This article, which Rita had initially read rather absentmindedly, now cast an exciting new light on this topic, motivating her, on her return home, to repeat Hamburger's experiments and test his conclusions. She certainly could never have imagined that her subsequent research in this direction would determine her future.

For the next seventeen days she dissected a few embryos every six hours, coming to some startling conclusions.[60] Her close analysis of the slices of tissues under her microscope suggested different explanations from the ones proposed by Hamburger. And this was thanks to the silver-staining techniques she had learned so well from Professor Levi.

She wrote a paper about her experiments, which was later

printed in *Archives de Biologie*, a prestigious Belgian journal, since Jewish researchers were forbidden to publish in Italian scientific periodicals at the time. Years later, Rita wondered how she had found the enthusiasm to solve small neurological and embryological issues at a time when German armies were advancing through Europe trying to destroy all of Western civilization. The answer was in the desperate and partially unconscious desire of human beings to ignore what is happening in situations where full awareness might lead one to self-destruction.[61]

The horror of war had taken on global dimensions, forcing her to protect her sanity by working uninterruptedly. During the initial Nazi occupation of Russia, Hitler had ordered the extermination of over three million prisoners of war, flouting every international war convention. In Germany the "Jewish problem" was being resolved by deporting Jews en masse to concentration camps, where equipment for mass liquidation was already in operation. As for Italy, there is no evidence that Mussolini finally decided on Jewish persecution under direct German pressure. On the contrary, we must conclude that the decision was spontaneous and exclusively his.[62] Meanwhile, recent episodes of discrimination and "Aryanization"—which conveniently entailed the transfer of Jewish property into Aryan hands in order to "de-Jew the economy"—opened the way to sensational cases of favoritism and corruption. The general directives issued by the new Ministry of Demography and Race were violently criticized within the party itself because racial policy rapidly became "a way for a corrupt gang to feed at the trough."[63]

Turin, considered a major economic and industrial hub,

was the first Italian city to be bombed and the Fiat Mirafiori plant was the intended target. From 1940 to 1945 the city was bombed more than fifty times. In spite of its systematic heavy air raids, it was still possible for Rita to live in Turin in early 1941. She was leading an intensely private, secluded life, trying to protect her anonymity. When the air raid alarm sounded, everybody would retreat to their basements and cellars with the most precious things they owned, like jewels and paintings, while Rita would regularly carry her Zeiss binocular microscope and some of her most precious silver-stained embryonic sections. These episodes lasted for hours, and the women would pray until the "all-clear" sirens announced that the danger was over. Very often, however, they had to rush down again because of a second, even worse attack. Sixteen hundred tons of explosives are estimated to have been dropped on northern Italy in 1941 and 1942, while in the rest of Europe, the threat from the air intensified with the arrival of "carpet bombing," which caused the total destruction of cities and monuments as well as the inevitable mass slaughter of civilians.

In the second part of 1942 and in 1943, the situation became even worse. It was no longer possible to ignore the spreading horror of the war. In Russia, the collapse of the Don Front marked the ruinous end of the Italian expedition. Forced by the Nazi-fascists to mount an impossible resistance, the Italian soldiers were abandoned without orders or equipment and died unburied on the frozen steppe. In Poland, the Germans razed the Jewish ghetto of Warsaw to the ground after the desperate revolts of the surviving prisoners. In North Africa the Italian colonies were finally abandoned by the Axis forces, who surrendered en masse to the Allies. A few months later the Americans and the British had occupied the whole of Sicily.

In protest against the relentless monstrosity of the racial laws, a greater number of Jews had decided to emigrate. According to Joshua Zimmerman's seminal book *Jews in Italy Under Fascist and Nazi Rule*, about six thousand Italian Jews left Italy between the passing of the racial laws in 1938 and the German invasion of Italy in 1943.

Among those who decided to leave, there was a significant contingent of Jews who, after the Italian-German alliance, had become partisans. According to R. J. B. Bosworth's *Mussolini's Italy: Life Under the Fascist Dictatorship, 1915–1945*, there were about two hundred thousand Italian partisans—of whom about thirty-five thousand were women—fighting a guerrilla war against the fascists and the Germans, and helping Allied soldiers free Italy from German occupation.

During that time, the United States in particular became the recipient of a mass emigration, largely of intellectuals, some of whom would become national figures. Among those who left Italy was physicist Enrico Fermi. He used the occasion of the conferral of his Nobel Prize in 1938 in Stockholm, to emigrate, along with his Jewish wife, Laura Capon, and settle permanently in Chicago. There he led the team responsible for inventing the first self-sustaining nuclear reactor, a line of research that would also result in the atomic bomb.

Others—like Rita's family—preferred to wait and see how things evolved. Some endured persecution in dignified silence, remaining faithful to their religion, while others dissociated themselves by converting to Catholicism. Very few people were able to preserve serenity in front of the irrational cataclysm that was overcoming Italy. Again, *The Second Coming* by W. B. Yeats comes to mind:

> *Things fall apart; the centre cannot hold;*
> *Mere anarchy is loosed upon the world,*
> *The blood-dimmed tide is loosed, and everywhere*
> *The ceremony of innocence is drowned;*
> *The best lack all conviction, while the worst*
> *Are full of passionate intensity.*[64]

In late 1941 the bombing of Turin intensified so dramatically that many of the upper-middle-class inhabitants left town. The Levi-Montalcini family moved into a small house in the hills near Asti, in Piedmont, an hour away from their hometown. Rita's lab became more cramped than ever, confined to a small table in the corner of the so-called dining room. Obtaining eggs was harder, too. She had to cycle from one hill to another, begging farmers to sell her some "for her babies." She was looking for fertilized eggs, which were more nutritious. One day, however, her brother, Gino, discovered that after she had done her experiments, she would use the same eggs to prepare meals for the family. From that day on, Gino categorically excluded eggs from his diet.

While Rita and her family were listening to the radio on July 25, 1943, at 10:45 p.m. the program was suddenly interrupted.

The unexpected news that the fascist rule was over, after twenty-one years of dictatorship, filled them with unprecedented elation and relief. Mussolini had been summoned by King Victor Emmanuel III and informed of the vote of no confidence given by the Grand Council of Fascism. Il Duce was forced to resign as prime minister and secretary of state in favor of Pietro Badoglio, marshal of Italy and new head of the government.

The fall of fascism was welcomed by the Jews with greater jubilation than by other Italians: For them it meant a double liberation both from fascist tyranny and from persecution. Yet, in spite of the fact that its leader was arrested and taken to prison, the controversial Department of Demography and Race continued to function and, more importantly, so did the racial legislation. Badoglio thought it was impossible at that time to bring about the overt termination of the racial laws without a violent clash with the Germans, or to be precise, with Hitler. Rather than radically abolish the laws, he decided that for the time being, they would not be enforced.[65] He did not, however, honor specific commitments as stated in his memoirs. On the contrary, with the exception of a few administrative changes, there was no softening of the fascist laws. Rita believed that July 25, 1943, indeed marked the end of an era, but it proved also to be the beginning of a most dramatic period, with German troops massing on the Italian frontier. The events that followed were more chaotic and alarming than ever.

After Mussolini was arrested, the most vital question was whether Italy would continue to fight alongside Germany or surrender to the Allies. Publicly, Victor Emmanuel III and

Badoglio claimed that Italy would continue the war as a member of the Axis forces. Privately, both men began secret negotiations. A few months later, on September 8, Italy signed an armistice stipulating its surrender to the Allied forces. Within a few hours German troops occupied the country, hungry for revenge, with the intention of punishing all the Jews as scapegoats for Italy's betrayal.

September 8, 1943, indeed marked the beginning of the final act in the immense tragedy of the Italian Jews. That same night, the king, along with Badoglio and their entourage, traveled from Pescara to Brindisi, closer to the Allies. Their departure was not hindered by the German troops stationed there, pleased to see them abandon most of the country to them. As an immediate consequence, the fascist generals handed big cities like Milan and Turin over to the Germans, ordering their troops to remain passive in order to avoid bloodshed.

Two days later, on September 10, when Rita saw German tanks outside Turin's central railway station, she knew that a delay of days, perhaps even hours, in leaving her hometown might cost her family their lives. While the Italian royal family and chief generals had shamefully fled, leaving most of the country in a state of chaos and anarchy, German troops were ferociously pouring down from the Alps through the Brennero Pass and spreading, unopposed, through northern Italy.

Rita's brother, Gino, and his wife, Maria (known as Mariuccia by the family), returned immediately from their honeymoon. Her sister Nina's family, after a thousand vicissitudes, managed to cross the frontier and sought refuge in

Switzerland. Rita and the others gave up and turned back, deciding to head south in the hope of an early liberation at the hands of the British and Americans, who were by then in control of Sicily and moving up the Italian peninsula.

Their final destination was the outcome of pure chance. In the carriage in which they were traveling, Rita found herself face-to-face with a fellow student from her medical student days wearing a fascist uniform. Rita could not admit that her family did not know where they were going; instead she told him that in a hurry, they had boarded the wrong train and therefore had to get off at the next station, Santa Maria Novella in Florence.[66] She ignored his skeptical remarks and experienced a tremendous relief in getting off the train, with the immediate aim of finding temporary lodging for the night. At six o'clock in the morning, she and her family were standing under pouring rain with no idea of where to go. Paola remembered that she had a friend who lived there, so they called her, asking for help. She directed the whole family to Signora Consilia Leoncini, a woman who was willing to rent a room provided they were not Jews. They were supposed to stay for one night; instead, after showing her false identity cards and assuring her they were all Catholics, they stayed until May 1945. Rita, Paola, and their mother had assumed the surname of Lupani while Gino and Mariuccia chose that of Locatelli. Their fake ID cards were a blessed result of Rita's foresight: On the eve of their sudden departure from Piedmont, Rita had decided to design counterfeit ID cards that were printed for her by her partisan friends in Turin, by then the most active center of anti-fascist resistance.

She distributed them to all her friends who managed to reach Florence. Though the cards lacked one of the necessary stamps, they could have saved their lives had they fallen into the hands of the Nazis; moreover, these fake IDs entitled them to purchase a daily ration of food. Though the cards were brazenly false, as people were perfectly aware, the sensitive Florentines were careful not to ask any embarrassing questions.[67]

Signora Consilia and her family proved to be convinced anti-fascists, and though from the very beginning she had suspicions about her lodgers' true identities, she pretended otherwise and played along, accepting all the risks this entailed. With her daughter Cosetta and son-in-law Ernesto, she would join Rita and her "Lupani" family to listen every night to the BBC, anxiously following the news of the bloody battle around the monastery of Montecassino, southeast of Rome, where German military forces had established the 160-kilometer (100-mile) Gustav Line from the Tyrrhenian sea to the Adriatic coast in order to prevent Allied troops from advancing northward. On February 15, 1944, American-led air raids almost completely destroyed the Benedictine abbey; finally British and American troops could advance up the Italian peninsula.

Rita had left her microscope in Turin, along with all of her necessary tools. As it was impossible for her to go on with her research, she and Paola spent their days forging false identity cards, helping other Jewish people risking deportation. A new sense of unity had emerged, deeper and more tangible than the one fascism had broken. Her forced life in hiding had started by allowing her to make her own proud contribution to the Resistance movement and gave her the unexpected chance to meet "Professor Lovisatto" once more. Under a false identity and after risking arrest several times, Professor Levi had decided to move with his wife and children to Fiesole, close to Florence, living not far from Rita's family. During the next several months, the two of them spent most of their time editing a revised edition of his two-volume textbook on histology, which Rita managed to salvage after a state of emergency was proclaimed, limiting freedom of movement during the day and imposing a curfew for all residents at night. Paola, constantly watching from a window the flight of fearful, anguished people from one part of the city to another, decided to immortalize them in one of her semi-abstract works, known as *A Walking City.*[68]

As German troops relentlessly marched into northern Italy, they liberated Mussolini from imprisonment on the Gran Sasso in a daring glider raid, proclaiming him head of the Italian Social Republic (RSI), better known as the Republic of Salò, a fascist puppet state based in the town of Salò on Lake Garda. From that moment in September 1943, two regimes tragically coexisted in Italy: the RSI in the north, led by Mussolini collaborating with the Germans, and a pro-Allied government in the south under Badoglio. Some of the leading fascists, including Mussolini's son-in-law, the former Minister of Foreign Affairs Galeazzo Ciano, were tried as conspirators by a fascist firing squad for having signed a motion requesting Mussolini's resignation, which had led to the end of the regime.

The policies of the new RSI were either dictated by the Germans or by their fiercely anti-Semitic agent, Giovanni

Preziosi, who believed that Jews were, ipso facto, foreigners and enemies.

Mussolini's ideas were more moderate. He wanted to herd all the Jews into Italian internment camps and postpone any solution of the problem until after the end of the war. This herding together often took place in schools and public buildings, and excluded people over seventy and the very sick, as well as "Aryanized" and "mixed" Jews. Here the interned Jews were treated with a degree of consideration and could receive packages from friends and family. Strict orders that the Jews were to remain in Italian camps and not be handed over to the Germans were issued in particular to Fossoli, near Modena, the largest concentration camp organized by the fascists before the extermination camps. Though these instructions were clear enough, the German commanders predictably disregarded them.

Moreover, the precarious financial and economic conditions of the RSI encouraged the legal confiscation of Jewish property to indemnify those who had lost everything during the Allied bombings. In other words, fascist authorities gave anti-Semitic persecution more of an economic character while attempting to maintain a relatively humane attitude toward other aspects of the Jews' situation, and trying to avoid deportations outside of Italy.[69] Giovanni Preziosi, named chief inspector for race, had been granted full powers for a Gestapo-like police activity in any sector of national life. He strove for a more rigorous application of existing laws, aiming at the total elimination of the Jews and the confiscation of their property. Mussolini, after some hesitation, was forced to capitulate. Ultimately, in the chaos following liberation achieved by Allied forces in 1945, many of those responsible for persecution were subjected to summary popular justice, with Preziosi committing suicide.

Meanwhile, the German army responded to partisan activity with violence and reprisals. A series of massacres of civilians and partisans accompanied the German occupation and gradual retreat up the peninsula during the eighteen months that it took the Allies to liberate the whole of Italy. Though the lack of sufficient troop numbers in southern Italy did not permit the Germans to enact their merciless extermination plans in full, they tried to grab as many Jews as possible along their path, including those interned in the south by the fascists.

The conditions of the Italian camps were not particularly harsh compared to those in other European countries, except for overcrowding and being mainly located in small, isolated towns in southern Italy. In the camp of Agnone, near Isernia, almost fifty interned Jews slept in the same dormitory, with no ventilation or heating. Fortunately, many Jews managed to escape on the day of the armistice, thanks to widespread, if undeclared, solidarity.

After September 8, 1943, the Nazis quickly resolved to include Italy in the "final solution," issuing an order to deport all Jews to Germany for extermination. Fascist authorities passively accepted this, becoming—unforgivably—de facto accomplices. On one hand, the hunt for Jews directly involved local authorities, civilians, and military; on the other hand, especially in northern Italy, the overwhelming majority of Italians gave the

Jews every kind of assistance at the risk of their own lives, by hiding them and, if possible, procuring false documents in the hope of impeding searches. Many hundreds of Jews had remained confidently at home, disbelieving even the advance signals until, immediately after the armistice, they saw actual proof of what the Germans intended to do. Having been informed that they sometimes demanded ransoms in exchange for immunity, a number of Jews were inclined to believe that all one had to do was pay to save one's life. Very few attempted to escape. Panic and terror struck everyone after the first large-scale roundups, but by then it was too late. The total number of those deported from Italy between 1943 and 1945 was over eight thousand. Of these, only six hundred and ten were able to return from the hell of the *lagers* (concentration camps); almost seven thousand died in captivity.[70]

It turned out to be a blessing in disguise that Rita and her family were hiding in Florence rather than Rome, where the overall situation was far more dangerous.

In the capital the Jews were mostly concentrated in the ghetto and naively hoped that they would be spared by the Nazis. On August 14, 1943, Rome was declared an open city as it had abandoned all resistance; therefore, the city was supposed to be peacefully occupied. Nonetheless, the Germans asked the Jews for the payment of over fifty kilograms of gold, giving them some hope of security. Most of the gold collected consisted of rings, necklaces, and other small objects that were everything the poor families of the Roman ghetto had. Once in possession of the gold, the Germans instead began enacting the second part of their criminal plan by plundering, completely undisturbed, a collection of books of immense historical and commercial value and other treasures belonging to the Roman synagogue. At dawn on October 16, 1943, the German police surrounded the ghetto and all the Jews were taken away indiscriminately. Some, who had been tipped off in advance, were able to save themselves in time; others took their lives to avoid arrest.

Within a few days, over one thousand arrested Jews were sent north, and from there to the extermination camps of Dachau and Auschwitz. Once the raid on people was completed, the plunder of their possessions continued apace—homes, stores, and warehouses were ransacked. Given the number of victims, the Rome ghetto tragedy was the most poignant large-scale raid, but dramatic arrests happened also in Venice, Genoa, Florence, and Trieste. Among the most fortunate were those who, due to local emergencies, were not immediately sent to the transit camps and remained in prison or smaller internment camps in certain parts of Italy, such as in Liguria, where workers for road repairs were badly required. Despite the pitiless manhunt, thousands of Jews managed to save their lives.

Fascism threw Italy into a moral and material abyss from which there was no exit, except through further degradation. Fascism's end was contained in its very origins, its own logic, with its anti-democratic and anti-liberal ideology requiring the suppression of freedom, with its lack of respect for the most elementary values of humanity, and with its illusory conviction of being the unique representative of the destiny and true will of the Italian people.[71] Mussolini sacrificed the Italian Jews on the altar of his alliance with Hitler, without giving it too much thought. They were just inexpensive pawns in a wider, pragmatically strategic chessboard.

More and more Jews were sent straight from Italy on trains to concentration camps in Poland and Germany, where for most of them there was no return. Among the survivors was one of Rita's close family friends, young chemist and future writer Primo Levi.[72] After the Soviet Army liberated Auschwitz in 1945, Levi returned to Turin, as reported in his 1963 memoir *La tregua* (*The Truce*). In his earlier, unique book, *Se questo è un uomo* (*If This Is a Man*, 1947), he describes his arrest as a member of the anti-fascist resistance in December 1943 and his first confinement in a labor camp in Fossoli. The most compelling part of the book deals with his incarceration in February 1944 in Auschwitz, the notorious death camp in Nazi-occupied Poland. When he arrived there after four days of traveling in a cramped cattle train—in his carriage, there were forty-five people, of whom only five managed to return—he was deprived of his name, dignity, and hope. He instantly became a *stuck* ("piece"), a prisoner: *Häftling* 174517. The number tattooed on his left arm recorded his date of admission, train of arrival, and nationality. Of the six hundred and fifty Italian Jews in his transport, Primo Levi was one of twenty who left the camp alive, thanks to his unique inner strength, which allowed him to survive in order to let the world know about the demonic situation of the *lager* and his spiritual and even physical metamorphosis. Levi's experiences as a slave laborer for eleven months and his ten-month struggle to return to Turin shaped the rest of his life.[73] Rita felt such respect and deference for his suffering that she dedicated the epilogue of her autobiography to this special friend of hers, thanking him for the unique legacy he left to the world. She believed that his message contained deep awareness of the harm one human being can inflict on another, but at the same time conveyed a message of hope, since he had managed to survive the most atrocious abuse.

One who did not make it home was Giuseppe Pagano, a prominent Jewish architect of the time and a close friend of Rita's brother, Gino. After graduating in architecture at the University of Turin, he became known for his involvement in the movement of rationalist architecture, along with Gino, leaving a remarkable mark on the history of Italian architecture and design of the early twentieth century. In the late 1930s he decided to leave the Fascist Party, realizing how the racist laws and the political propaganda had radically corrupted it. He was not a transformist for personal interests; in fact, quite the opposite. He lived the drama of political disappointment and radical realignment, becoming a determined partisan as soon as the Nazi troops invaded Italy after the armistice.[74]

Rita was so upset by his unfortunate fate that she dedicated a whole chapter to him in her book *Senz'olio, contro vento* (*Fearlessly Sailing Against the Wind*). Arrested in 1944, Pagano managed to escape with the utmost courage after liberating 260 other prisoners and reaching Milan in civilian clothes. However, being unable to adapt himself to a cautious, secluded, clandestine life, he was imprisoned again, at San Vittore, Milan, and then transferred to Mauthausen, Austria, where he died a martyr's death under torture for having defended a deported companion. His greatest aspiration, tragically unfulfilled, was to survive and return in order to write about the inferno of the concentration camp and dedicate the rest of his life to erasing the hatred among human beings.[75]

Ironically enough, he died at the age of forty-eight, only three days before April 25, 1945, the historic date when the Allies and their partisan supporters drove the Germans out of northern Italy, thus liberating the country.

Another close friend of the Levi-Montalcini family was writer and translator Leone Ginzburg, who had married Natalia, Professor Levi's youngest daughter. In 1940, Natalia and Leone, already deprived of their Italian citizenship, received the fascist punishment known as *confino*, or internal exile, to a remote, impoverished village in the Abruzzi region, where they stayed until 1943.[76] Somehow, Leone was able throughout this period to continue his work as head of the Einaudi publishing house he had co-founded in 1933. On November 20, 1943, Leone—then living under the false name of Leonida Gianturco—was arrested in Rome by the Italian police in the clandestine printing shop of a partisan underground newspaper, *L'italia Libera*. He was taken to the Regina Coeli prison, where he was subjected to severe torture. On February 5, 1944, he died there, at the age of thirty-four, from the injuries he had received.

In *Family Sayings*, Natalia Ginzburg wrote extensively about her husband's indomitable partisan engagement as well as about their close friendship with the anti-fascist writer and poet Cesare

Pavese, who, in 1935, was also arrested and sentenced in his turn to a period of confinement for possessing letters from a political prisoner.[77]

On August 3, 1944, a state of emergency was proclaimed in Florence. Electricity, water, and bread were unobtainable. With the exception of the Ponte Vecchio, all the bridges across the Arno had been blown up. This was a catastrophe for the Florentines, many of whom were cut off from local food supplies. A few days later, on August 11 at 6:00 a.m., the whole city of Florence rose against the Germans in a major coordinated insurrection. By September 2, Florence was liberated by the partisans and the Allied troops, in spite of the fact that the Germans had scattered a large quantity of mines all over the city, causing many deaths. Rita was finally able to show her identity card, regain her identity, and join the Red Cross, which she had dreamed of doing since she was a little girl, offering her services as a doctor at the Anglo-American quarters. Along with Giuseppe Levi's son Alberto, she was assigned to work in the refugee camps set up outside the city.

Her task was to take care of not only those displaced by the war, but also to monitor the health of farmworkers who had been forced by the bombings to leave villages in the Apennines, south of Bologna, and were being treated in old military barracks just outside of Florence. Hundreds of them, sleeping on straw mattresses, packed the soldiers' dormitories and what had once been stables for their horses.

Under the circumstances, Rita became a nurse and a doctor at the same time, working day and night. Many newborn babies and children were suffering from the cold, malnutrition, and dehydration, and Rita found herself helplessly witnessing their inevitable suffering and death, reliving the anguish she had felt during Giovanna's illness. Her own family struggled, too. Her brother Gino's wife, Mariuccia, had been going through hardships since giving birth to their first child. Mariuccia had difficulties in breastfeeding and milk was very difficult to get until the arrival of the Allies, who started distributing powdered milk. Moreover, toward the end of the winter, an epidemic of abdominal typhoid, caused by contaminated drinking water, spread within a few days, and since there were no antibiotics at that time, the number of casualties rose to up to fifty a day.[78] By then Rita was spending most of her time attending only the most seriously ill. She was risking a lethal contagion every day. Deep in her heart she would have liked to take a more active role in the partisan resistance, but her "constitutional ineptitude," as Gino often pointed out, precluded a "conspiratorial life."

After witnessing the painful death of a twenty-year-old girl from a bacterial infection, Rita decided once and for all that she did not have the necessary emotional detachment to be a medical doctor. Even though she continued working for the Health Service until May of the following year, she knew she could not practice the profession and that, given her sensitive nature, she should return to the path of medical research at the lab.

On April 28, 1945, Mussolini, disguised as a German officer, tried to escape and was shot by partisans—as Rita's father Adamo had predicted, comparing Il Duce to Cola di Rienzo, the fourteenth-century Roman tribune who, after committing abuses and crimes, was killed by the same mob who had exalted him.

Fascism, along with Nazism, made corpses of many, including in the end the two architects of their inhuman regimes. Mussolini was hung upside down in Piazzale Loreto, Milan, displayed for the vituperation of those who had once been happy to cheer him. His death apparently influenced Hitler to commit suicide shortly afterward.

Fascism was finally defeated. In July of that year, Rita returned to northern Italy with Gino in a military truck, then proceeded on rented bicycles to Asti to check on their relatives before going on to Turin. They found the city eager to repair the damage left by the war and restore its former dignity. There would be no more graffiti exalting Il Duce. Turin, in fact, soon regained its severe monarchic appearance, as Giorgio de Chirico had vividly described it.

After the horror of the racial laws was over, Rita wanted to dedicate her life to scientific research, possibly as an assistant of Professor Levi at the University of Turin, which was now ready to welcome them both back. She was offered her previous position, as assistant, and Rodolfo Amprino was available to share neurobiological experiments as before. However, the war had left a deep scar and it was difficult for Rita to regain the enthusiasm for science that had sustained her through the atrocities of the war. She had to force herself out of the state of depression she had fallen into and adjust herself to a radical change of scenario in her personal and professional life. In a way, she had to reinvent herself.

She became increasingly aware of the inadequacy of her scientific training and enrolled in a biology course, thinking she lacked sufficient aptitude to be accepted in the faculties of physics or mathematics.[79] It was at that time that she followed the academic successes of Salvador Luria, by then a professor at the University of Indiana in Bloomington. She had read several articles about him and his achievements in scientific magazines and Italian newspapers.

At the same time Rita became reacquainted with Renato Dulbecco, who had just come back from Russia, where he had served as a medical doctor and shared in the horrific defeat of the Italian troops. Rita had been impressed from the very beginning by his talent for mathematics and physics. She suggested that he enroll in the physics department, advising him to take an assistant position with Professor Levi so that he would have more time to study physics—and Levi duly offered him a post.

Subsequently, Rita's deep sense of friendship and respect led her to write to Luria, by then chairman of the University of Indiana's biology department, asking if he could offer Renato the opportunity of working for a year at his university in the rapidly expanding field of genetics. In the summer of 1946, Luria offered Dulbecco a fellowship.

At the same time, Rita was called by Professor Levi into his office to read a letter that he had just received from Viktor

Hamburger of Washington University, St. Louis, who was curious about Rita's conclusions, entirely different from his own. After reading her articles in Belgian and Swiss journals, Hamburger wrote to Levi asking if Rita could spend a semester in St. Louis to investigate the issue further with him. She was honored by the invitation, but did not want to interrupt the biological studies she had just embarked on with Rodolfo Amprino, so she accepted but postponed her departure to the following year. Those days spent with Rodolfo in the full flush of their reconquered scientific energy were among the most serene in her career.

On September 19, 1947, Rita and Renato set out together for the United States, where in different environments they would pursue scientific research that would lead both of them to the Nobel Prize.

Chapter Six

CROSSING THE ATLANTIC

A year after completing her research with Rodolfo, Rita sailed from Genoa to North America on board a Polish ship, the *Sobieski*. While Renato Dulbecco was heading for the University of Indiana, she was on her way to St. Louis, Missouri. A new life was ahead for both of them on the new continent. It was truly an honor for Rita to have been asked to work with Professor Hamburger, considered by the scientific community to be the founder of developmental neurobiology, or neuroembryology—the study of the nervous system's development before birth. He was responsible for making the chick embryo the standard research subject in the field. Before offering Rita the fellowship, he had consulted professor Salvador Luria, who spoke highly of her tenacity and reliability. Moreover, she was eager to see the country she had heard so much about and have the opportunity of meeting some of the most prominent scientists in her field.

Renato, too, was entirely oriented toward his new career.

While most travelers on board were enjoying the outdoor swimming pool for long hours during their two-week voyage, Rita and Renato would find shelter indoors and discuss the prospects before them. Renato was thirty-three, handsome, charming, and already married, determined to settle down in the United States; he intended, as soon as the right opportunity presented itself, to have his wife and two children join him from Turin. Rita was thirty-eight and eager to make the most of the prestigious invitation she had received. She had resolved, however, that she would return to Turin at the end of the six or nine months of work offered by Professor Hamburger, since neither her mother nor Paola would have ever considered leaving Italy.

Rita knew, once and for all, that she could not adjust her own life and work to the needs of others. She did not intend to repeat her mother's experience of submission by getting married and having children; she was ready to concentrate instead on her life's work. Her career had already been delayed by a decade because of her father's opposition to her seeking a university education and by the Second World War. She was sorry to leave Professor Levi and, even more so, her family, but she was confident that these months across the Atlantic would go by very quickly.

Rita and Renato were both ambitious and aware that to make a career far away from home was a very challenging goal, yet they shared each other's dreams and were confident they would succeed. They were gradually becoming very close. They had graduated in the same session at the University of Turin in 1936, and while crossing the ocean they developed a special friendship that continued to grow in the years to come.

When the *Sobieski* at last reached New York after twelve days and twelve nights, a crewmember announced over the loudspeaker that passengers should not rush to one side of the ship, because two years earlier an ocean liner had been at risk of capsizing when most of the passengers rushed to the railing to look at the Statue of Liberty.[80] They were welcomed by a spectacular sunset and they spent their first American night still on board.

The following day, the tedious process of disembarking took almost eight hours. Like other immigrants, Rita had to be scrutinized, along with her papers and luggage, at the immigration service desk. This brought to her mind the painful experience of thousands of Jewish people who had escaped persecution during the fascist period by reaching New York Harbor. Once they were free to go, Renato went on to Bloomington, while Rita spent two days with her cousin Luciana and her family in New Jersey, happily seizing the opportunity of visiting some well-known sights such as the Empire State Building, where she felt as excited as if she were on the highest crests of the Alps.

She then proceeded to St. Louis on board a luxury train called the *Spirit of St. Louis*, named after Charles Lindbergh's historic solo crossing of the Atlantic. With its seats covered in blue velvet, it was the most elegant train she had ever been on, and it was impossible for her not to remember her journey on a cattle train during the war when she had first read Professor Hamburger's article. She was also reminded of her early passion for trains when, as a child, she spent many hours at Turin's central station, observing the intense traffic of locomotives while dreaming of unknown, boundless countries and the great trip her father had promised her when "the little girls reached the age of thirteen."[81] Moreover, *The Book of Trains*, her favorite reading whenever she was sick as a child, connected railroads with convalescence and recovery. This train journey acted as a powerful uplifting experience after the challenges and deprivations she had faced during the war.

On a hot afternoon in early autumn, she left the train, marking the occasion by fixing in her mind the hands of a big tower clock at St. Louis's railway station. The city appealed to her with its stately atmosphere, its characteristic architecture dating back to the beginning of the century. In fact, St. Louis had been the site of the 1904 World's Fair, also called the Louisiana Purchase Exposition, and many buildings from that time had been preserved. Located along the impressive Mississippi River, the city boasted a population of about two million people. It had once been the starting point for wagon trains carrying settlers across the prairies and deserts, a gateway to the West.

Rita arrived by taxi at the main entrance of Washington University, which captivated her even more than the local Catholic cathedral with its unique Tiffany stained-glass windows and impressive mosaics. At that time, the university—founded in 1853—could count six Nobel laureates in economics, physiology or medicine, chemistry, or physics, four having done the major part of their pioneering research there.

It was still Indian summer and Rita was overwhelmed by the autumnal colors of the maple trees, which had no parallel in the dull tones of the hills around Turin in the same season. For her, the sense of wonder associated with this explosion of colors before "falling into winter lethargy" signaled a positive change in her existence after the dark trials she had survived. Immediately, Rita felt at home and rejoiced in having found the perfect place to start a new phase of her career.

She was left at the entrance of the red brick Rebstock building, which housed the Zoology Institute. Unlike the other buildings on campus, it was attractively covered in ivy and marked by two majestic oak trees. Located on an elevation overlooking Forest Park, it became the special pride of St. Louis. From the top of its steps, one could catch a glimpse of the medical school, which had by then attained a national reputation, and of the City Art Museum. Wide lawns spread between the Missouri red granite buildings and the paths were flanked by ginkgo trees, creating a dignified atmosphere without diminishing the relaxed informality of the campus. The university was about an hour away by bus from the city center and was practically always open, as daytime classes were followed uninterruptedly by evening courses for working students.

A smiling Professor Hamburger was waiting for her in the library on the second floor. His youthful appearance contrasted with his grey hair, but Rita felt immediately at ease because of her awareness that their backgrounds complemented each other. She was struck by his wisdom, dignity, generosity, and kindness. His mastery of the English language was impressive; at that time

Rita knew little English and she felt awkward at having to use her hands to make herself understood.

Following their hour-long conversation, Professor Hamburger invited Rita to take a short walk through Rebstock Hall. A three-story building located on the south side of the campus, facing Forsyth Boulevard, it was the center of the biology department. It housed the administration, a large auditorium, and a library. There was only one telephone for the whole department, in the booth of the secretary-librarian, and people were called to the phone by a bell; Viktor Hamburger's signal was two short rings.[82]

Rita was impressed not only by the intense rhythm of the school, but also by the informality of the American system of teaching, allowing professors and young instructors to hold their classes outdoors on warm days, sitting on the lawn with squirrels and birds all around. In the library, gum-chewing students would relax with their feet on the tables. She could not avoid thinking of Professor's Levi's spartan rules in contrast with this casual and peaceful atmosphere in her new American university.

She was asked to dinner at Professor Hamburger's home where she met Viktor's wife, Martha, who, unlike her husband and Rita, was not Jewish but of German origin. She was a woman of great intelligence and culture who aspired to a career in sociology. Later, a sudden breakdown confined her for many years to a mental institution, where she experienced the most inhumane therapy and psychic degradation. Rita became a family friend and would visit her with Viktor; she was impressed by the dignity with which Martha Hamburger was able to endure her ordeal.

After this welcoming dinner, Professor Hamburger took Rita to the house of a middle-age couple with whom she agreed to stay, given her limited financial resources. The landlady was a confirmed Republican and, without realizing Rita's background, openly expressed her ideas about politics and religion, which included a strong dislike of Jews. Despite this first experience of a typical Midwest mentality, Rita was sure that a more positive attitude would have certainly surfaced soon enough. She realized that, after all, she had landed in the right place, a potential Garden of Eden far from the stiff formality of European universities. This was one reason why her stay on this side of the Atlantic Ocean lasted—though with long intervals—for thirty years, not for only a semester, as she had planned.

Chapter Seven

RESEARCH YEARS IN ST. LOUIS

Viktor Hamburger and Rita Levi-Montalcini's backgrounds did indeed complement one another. From the start, and in spite of Rita's broken English, they established a productive collaboration and Professor Hamburger became a new mentor in her life, gradually acquiring the same level of importance as Professor Levi, if not greater.

Hamburger's field was experimental and analytical embryology, while Rita was a neurologist and an expert in silver impregnation and microsurgery. Under his supervision and guidance, she happily continued the research she had started at the university in Turin.[83] Their two fields converged into a particular discipline known as developmental biology— or simply embryology—which aimed to explore the different processes of development that had been clarified by recent technological developments.

Hamburger had studied at the University of Freiburg with

Hans Spemann, a German scientist who was awarded a Nobel Prize for his discovery of the so-called "organizers," special tissues that induce the formation of different organs if transplanted into earlier, formless embryos.

Historically, investigation of the structure and function of the brain had become possible after 1873 thanks to histologist Camillo Golgi, who invented a silver-containing stain that neurons absorbed, but the cells around them did not.[84] However, it was only with Spanish neurologist Santiago Ramón y Cajal that the first studies of the nervous system's developments before birth were carried out. He was one of the pioneering scientists to use chick embryos in early stages of development because chick neurons were very similar to those of humans and other mammals and they absorbed the silver stain very well. They provided an ideal subject because they were easily obtained and could be experimented with, even at home. In his autobiography, Ramón y Cajal explained why he had followed this path. Since the forest is usually impenetrable, he maintained, why not analyze the small plants at an early stage of growth when they are still at the nursery? He also underlined how fortunate it was that the method of silver impregnation made cells and nervous fibers visible in a very selective way at the initial stage of development rather than later at the adult level.

Golgi and Ramón y Cajal agreed on the structure of the brain but disagreed on the way the nervous system was organized. While Golgi proposed the network theory, Ramón y Cajal supported the cell-by-cell theory, which later proved to be more reliable because by then electron microscopes had revealed tiny gaps called synapses between connecting neurons (the name had been given to them by C. S. Sherrington, an English physiologist who played a pioneering role in the field of neurophysiology similar to the one Ramón y Cajal played in neuroanatomy).[85] Ramón y Cajal's extraordinary intuition led not only to the belief that every cell is an independent unit, but also to the discovery that the ends of its fibers are not in fact materially connected. The assumption of spatial discontinuities was particularly important for Rita's research as far as the function of the nervous system was concerned. Like most leading scientists, she, too, favored the cell-to-cell approach, also called the neuronal method.

Neurobiology and embryology, the two fields of research in which Rita and Professor Hamburger were engaged, came together in the work of Paul Weiss, an Austrian researcher who emigrated to the United States in 1931. He attributed to the cells, to the neuronal circuits, and to nerve tissues an almost unlimited capacity of adapting to environmental stimuli, both in the central and peripheral nervous systems.

This theory was challenged and eventually refuted by Roger Sperry, Hamburger's "rebellious" graduate student, with simple but rigorous methodologies. He studied the behavior of rats whose nerves had been sectioned and then reconnected with muscles with opposite functions, as well as of fish and amphibians that had undergone surgical severing of the optic nerve. His conclusions, based on the principles previously asserted by

Ramón y Cajal, proved that nerve fibers are governed during their growth not in a chaotic, random way, but according to a rigidly predetermined genetic program.

Professor Hamburger and Rita finally met both Weiss and Sperry in Chicago in 1949, at the first conference ever organized in the newly established field of neurobiology, an ambitious three-day project attended by very few pioneer participants. Sperry encountered great difficulties in pursuing his experiments in clear opposition to the theories of his direct superior, Professor Weiss, but thirty-two years later he would be awarded a Nobel Prize for his studies on neuronal specificity and the different functions of the two hemispheres of the brain. While these topics sounded almost like pure science fiction in March 1949, they started an irreversible process of innovative transformation. This biology sector that had been considered very static suddenly emerged as one of the most dynamic fields of research. Rita gradually considered herself blessed and privileged to have been able to witness and participate actively in this ground-breaking metamorphosis.

Hamburger's early research on determining how grafting and removing limbs on chick embryos affected the growth of nerves going from the spinal cord to the limbs followed the guidelines imparted by Weiss and Sperry. It was this particular research that had inspired Rita in 1940, while riding in a cattle car on a beautiful summer day, to plunge into a new challenge in her makeshift home lab and come to different conclusions. Seven years later she was having the unique opportunity to persevere in this direction and verify any progress with the master himself and other international scientists.

During the first weeks of her stay in St. Louis, Rita happily found a new accommodation, not with a fervent Republican but with an ardent Democrat, Mrs. Elizabeth Gray, who clearly rejoiced at Truman's election. Her English was elegant and witty. Every evening she would check if Rita had come home safe and sound from the office since she always walked back late at night. They soon became friends, and one day Rita tried to explain the research she was involved in. Her hostess listened with great attention, but in the end, commented, "It is a splendid research, I am proud of you. What I have not understood yet is whether these experiments are done on the yolk or on the albumen."

Mrs. Gray was hopeless in science. As Rita reported in one of the numerous long letters she wrote to her family, for her hostess eggs were simply ingredients for a tasty frittata, as for her brother, Gino. Luckily, as it was no longer wartime, when eggs had been extremely scarce, Rita did not need to beg farmers to sell her some or plunder the family fridge to get the chick's embryos for her experiments.

In spite of her arduous research schedule, Rita made sure to take the time to discover the history of St. Louis.

In 1763–64, Pierre Laclède and Auguste Chouteau, two French traders, settled at the confluence of the Mississippi and Missouri Rivers and established a flourishing post for fur trading with the local native tribes. Laclède managed to assume a position of civil control by granting new settlers parcels of land in town and the surrounding countryside during what was originally called "the golden age of St. Louis." The early French families built the town's economy until 1803, when the United States, under President Thomas Jefferson, acquired the whole territory from France as part of the Louisiana Purchase. The Territory of Louisiana was renamed Missouri in 1812.

Starting that year, immigrant families from Italy, Germany, and Ireland arrived in St. Louis and opened new businesses, including printing and banking. In the mid-1820s the town's economy blossomed, largely due to the introduction of steamboats and other ships, which soon transformed the area into a bustling inland port. This improved connections with New Orleans and eastern markets while the fur trade continued to be its major industry. Among St. Louis's many glories, according to Rita, were its having joined the anti-slave Union side of Abraham Lincoln in the Civil War and offering refuge to Blacks fleeing from the South, who brought their music with them, mainly blues and early jazz.[86]

Most of the Italian immigrants came from Piedmont, but later a new wave from southern Italy also settled in St. Louis's Little Italy, located in midtown, an area called The Hill. The Italians stayed united despite their different dialects and customs, and seldom intermarried. In that particular part of the city, typical Italian specialties and produce were readily available; during the summer, usually on Sundays, residents would sing, dance, and enjoy eating ice cream. The whole community had imported a sort of nationalistic right-wing pride from their homeland. They considered Mussolini a great Italian political figure, and Guglielmo Marconi was often referred to as a scientist who had honored the glorious period of fascism with his genius.

Rita thought the Italians in St. Louis had identified their patriotic feelings with fascist ideology. She soon met the Italian consul, but after she heard him openly express his disapproval of the partisans who had fought in the Resistance, she preferred not to see him again. One meeting was enough for her to decide she had to look elsewhere for friends. On principle, she carefully avoided talking about politics. She was all alone, and did not have any relatives in Missouri to count on, but often spent her Sundays visiting Silvia and Paolo Rava, a couple who shared her background and cultural interests. He was a lawyer, and Rita gradually began to turn to him for advice on legal issues after she accepted a position at Washington University.

She also loved reading. Among her favorite books was Cesare Pavese's *La luna e i falò* (*The Moon and the Bonfires*, 1950), the last novel by the great Turinese writer. This book on migration, identity, and nostalgia was one that she came to appreciate after her arrival in the New World, far from her native Piedmont. By translating Herman Melville's *Moby Dick* and modern English-language authors from James Joyce to William Faulkner, Pavese had defied the fascist regime to open new horizons for Italian contemporary fiction. And this was very important for Rita at this stage. Besides the fiction and poetry she had shared with her sister Nina since childhood, she greatly admired Primo Levi and Carlo Levi, as well as William Butler Yeats and Dylan Thomas.

She appreciated the visual arts, too, especially painting. Her favorite Italian contemporary artist was Alberto Burri, a medical doctor who became an artist while he was a prisoner of war in Texas in 1943. Whenever she could, she would visit galleries and attend art openings. She also loved classical music, from Bach and Mozart to Schubert and Chopin, often going to concerts and always listening to recordings at home, and on some special occasions at the lab. She accepted invitations to dinners and parties, and started discovering other states by bus, train, and car. Driven by constant curiosity, she even optimistically ventured to Florida and Alabama, traveling for two days and on six different buses, mainly during the night, and found the whole experience interesting and entertaining.

An intense correspondence with her mother and sister Paola, back at home in Turin, started immediately after her arrival in St. Louis. She would give them a detailed report of her everyday routine and of all the places she managed to visit in long letters written in neat and clear handwriting, with no corrections and avoiding negative comments on the people she met, except for the occasional touch of irony. She wrote fifteen hundred letters, two hundred of which she published in a special selection entitled *Cantico di una vita* (*Canticle of a Lifetime*).[87]

Rita's pronounced affinity with her family led her, years later, to write a book entitled *Un universo inquieto* (*A Restless Universe*).[88] According to her, her sister's research was as daring as her own, even though Paola's fantastic world was not constrained by impenetrable laws while Rita often lacked any tangible, immediate results from her explorations and experiments with cells. Paola rarely moved from Turin while Rita traveled extensively, yet both their universes were in constant evolution. Their two restless parallel lives were driven by constant experimentation and creative freedom. Paola's dedication to art began when she was a little girl; Rita's scientific interests blossomed in her adolescence. Unlike Rita, Paola did not suffer a great deal from attending a school that offered no prospect of going on to university; she knew, since childhood, that she wanted to be an artist. Both sisters enjoyed great autonomy and a sense of independence, and clearly had a lot in common because Rita often used to describe people by referring to paintings she had come to appreciate largely through her sister. As examples, she compared the young scientist James Watson to the celebrated harlequin of Picasso's Blue Period, and her research associate Nando to a beautiful young monk in a painting by Titian. Not to mention Guido, her beloved nephew, whom she thought resembled a putto of Luca della Robbia.

Moreover, Rita's interdisciplinary approach to science belonged clearly to the right hemisphere of the brain, based mainly on intuition, dedication, and endurance rather than logic and strict analysis. She used to make sketches in her research and played classical music in the lab because it stimulated her mental processes. In the same way, Paola's paintings, at the beginning clearly figurative in the tradition of her master, Felice Casorati, became more geometric and abstract, especially after the devastating experience of the Second World War. She gradually became more inclined to systematically investigate her interior reality, the self. After Rita and Paola began living together in Rome starting in 1963, Paola's art became not only more scientific, but also somehow alchemical, in constant search of timeless signs of universal significance. And just as Paola's aesthetic did not comply with any specific prevailing trend or current, Rita did not belong to any academic circle; she persistently wanted to go beyond the bare facts accepted by her contemporaries, and was eager to welcome new challenges.

When Rita landed in the United States, she was a mature woman and already a respected scientist in the field of the nervous system's development. She was well known in the Italian scientific community for having published, along with Giuseppe Levi, several articles on neurogenesis in specialized publications. She was too independent to stay in Turin and soon came to appreciate the freedom Hamburger was giving her in her everyday routine. She also greatly respected the American academic environment and working conditions at Washington University, where results and merit were recognized and appreciated. Moreover, if she had gone back to Turin after a few months, what university would have offered her a tenured position? She was not part of any academic school; she cared for her own intellectual and scientific independence, as she proudly stressed in several of her letters. Moreover, she knew that research funding in Italy was limited, and this, in the long run, would have proven a great obstacle.

For her, scientific research was not a mere job but an irrepressible passion, a vocation, and a full-time engagement. This is the main reason why she decided, nine months after she arrived in the States, to skip, or rather postpone, her first summer holidays in Italy. She could not risk being left without the necessary visa to come back again. By then she knew it was far better for her to stay longer in St. Louis, always encouraged by her close confidante Paola. Though she missed her "American sister," Paola agreed that Rita had a higher chance of reaching her scientific goals in the States.

Rita was, in fact, invited to participate in international symposia, often as the only woman in an otherwise male scientific domain. Usually nicknamed "The Queen," Rita would proudly arrive without a king and, as she wrote to her family, if someone not knowing her well would ask if her husband was in the audience, she would wittily reply that she was her own husband. She was not, however, a lonely scientist at all. She chose to celebrate her fortieth birthday with friends from her days as a student at the University of Turin, such as Renato Dulbecco and Salvador Luria, whom she called Salva. Rita would constantly exchange ideas with them, especially at congresses, where she was most of the time the only woman speaker; the chairman would often be inclined to open the conference by saying "Lady and gentlemen," to which Rita would answer with an elegant bow.

Besides being in constant touch with her family, Rita made time to meet friends like the Ravas and establish new acquaintances. On the weekends she used to take part in picnics on a small boat on the lakes in the area, organized by her colleagues at the department and their wives, with whom she had excellent relationships. She would take Sunday trips as well on the *Admiral* down the Mississippi River, so different from the Po River she knew so well, leisurely savoring an ice cream cone and admiring the panorama of small islands. Through the trees, however, she could see another world, small houses and huts reflecting the poverty of the dwellers, like the slums in the down-town area, mainly inhabited by Blacks. At the same time, she would admire the classic architecture of the financial district of the city, including some prominent landmarks by Frank Lloyd Wright's mentor, Louis Sullivan, credited with developing the aesthetics and dynamics of the first skyscrapers.

She often went to Bloomington, not too far from St. Louis, to visit Salvador Luria and Renato Dulbecco, who had become her irreplaceable intellectual and emotional points of reference. It was not nostalgia that drove her, but the desire to interact with them and have the opportunity to talk about their research and her own. All of them had studied under Giuseppe Levi and shared an interest in molecular biology, in which biology interfaces with physics and chemistry.

Salvador Luria was born into an influential Italian Sephardic Jewish family and was only one year ahead of Rita. When the fascist regime banned all the Jews from academic research fellowships, he left Turin for Paris in 1938. When the German armies invaded France in 1940, Salvador fled on a bicycle to Marseille, where he obtained an immigration visa to the United States. With the help of physicist Enrico Fermi, he first won a Rockefeller Foundation fellowship at Columbia University and later taught for seven years at Indiana University in Bloomington. In 1969, Luria shared the Nobel Prize with Max Delbrück and Alfred Day Hershey for his seminal discoveries in the physiology and genetics of bacteria and viruses, which became important tools in genetic engineering.

Renato Dulbecco worked with Luria for two years at

Bloomington before moving to the California Institute of Technology (Caltech) in Pasadena to work directly with Max Delbrück, and then to the Salk Institute in La Jolla, California, where he became the president of that institution and continued to study the genetics of cancer until he retired. In 1975 he, too, was awarded the Nobel Prize in Physiology or Medicine along with Howard Temin and David Baltimore for their groundbreaking studies of viruses, including those that can cause cancer.

By 1947, Salvador Luria was a highly respected microbiologist. He therefore seemed the best person for Rita to consult about her future as a scientist, since it was he who had written a flattering letter to Professor Hamburger to recommend her. She believed that the most recent advances in genetics were laying down precise guidelines for the field that neurobiology, her specialty, did not possess.

She still had some "distressing" doubts about the validity of her own research and she confided in Salva openly and sincerely. He was young, tall, and black-haired, with sharp, penetrating eyes. He did his best to make her feel comfortable by speaking Piedmontese, though they both lacked fluency in that dialect, jokingly imitating a well-known family doctor to the Turin Jewish aristocracy. How did her old colleague react to Rita's confidences? He shared her perplexity about the future of neurobiology, which indeed seemed to progress very slowly vis-à-vis other disciplines such as genetics, biochemistry, and virology. His adamant advice was that she should persist in her research in experimental neuroembryology. He saw her predicament: She was too expert in her own field, but too inexperienced in others to easily change research fields at this point in her career. Rita recalled during an interview in 1987 with the Italian television journalist Maurizio Costanzo that Luria and Dulbecco considered her a sort of Cinderella; nevertheless, her tenacious optimism dispelled her doubts and allowed her to continue her research in the best working conditions in the Americas.

Both Luria and Dulbecco introduced her to some brilliant students in their departments. One of them, James Watson, not yet twenty, was to become one of the stars of genetic research. In fact, in 1962, he was awarded the Nobel Prize in Physiology or Medicine. Along with Watson, Max Delbrück, Alfred Hershey, and Dulbecco, Luria had initiated the so-called Phage Group, revealing how viruses passed on genetic information to cells they infected and how bacteria passed on traits that allowed them to resist the viruses, and thus opening the way to a new era in genetics.

While Luria and Dulbecco had chosen to experiment with very simple organisms like phages, microorganisms similar to viruses or cellular cultures in vitro, Rita instead experimented with chicken embryos, which were much more complex and required weeks instead of hours of investigation.

In the 1940s Rita knew very little about genetic programming, yet she could see how it would soon have a seminal influence on the development of the embryonic nervous system. Luria and Dulbecco also generously introduced her to two of their most illustrious colleagues, Hermann J. Muller, who had just won the Nobel Prize in Physiology or Medicine for his discovery of the mutation effects of X-ray radiation, and Tracy

Sonneborn, equally eminent in his own field. Rita was astonished and surprised by their availability and flattered by the attention they dedicated to her. She was relatively young, mid-career, and still easily impressed; in those years she considered this kind of distinguished scientist as belonging to an intellectually superior league.

Though she had often been discouraged, perplexed, and doubtful at the beginning, after the key meeting with Salva she came to the conclusion that she could not abandon the research she had started. She felt she had to reinvestigate, in more and more depth, the effects of amputation on the development of the nervous centers in charge of the innervation of the excised limbs of chick embryos. This was, after all, the very reason she had been invited to St. Louis.

The gradually improving results of her studies impressed Professor Hamburger to the point that he offered to extend the length of her appointment at Washington University. A slight raise in her salary allowed Rita to rent a larger apartment, shared with Anna Maria Conforto, a young Roman physicist, and surround herself with art—mainly paintings by Paola; a sculpture of her beloved governess Giovanna by her brother, Gino; and a few reproductions of masterpieces by El Greco. She became an excellent hostess and kept her apartment impeccable. No one would suspect that back in Turin she had once counted on a cook, a maid, and a chauffeur.

She loved entertaining her friends as she had previously done in Turin, where she had often invited artists like Giorgio de Chirico, Felice Casorati, and Lalla Romano. In St. Louis, her specialty was risotto with mushrooms, followed by a variety of Italian cheeses and vegetables, served with Italian red wine from different regions. A fresh fruit salad and homemade ice cream would conclude the meal, along with sweet dessert wine from California.

Rita finally got rid of all the insecurities of her painful childhood and adolescence to become the woman she wanted to be: more self-confident and aware of her unique role as a scientist in a new, challenging environment where everything was possible and the future was still to be written.

Her professional worries came to an end in an unexpected way one fortunate afternoon in late autumn of 1947. She was almost haphazardly looking under the microscope at the latest series of chick embryo sections, between the third and the seventh day of incubation, when neurons in the brain and spinal cords are just beginning to form. She was pleased at the way she had silver-salt-stained the nerve cells or neurons; they showed so clearly in the background. All of a sudden she realized how exceptionally dynamic this early stage of development was, and she was struck by the rapid changes in certain parts of the spinal cord over a day or even a few hours. In her mind's eye, she saw thousands of neurons in long lines, migrating from one place to another like colonies of birds, insects, or biblical locusts, while in other parts, masses of nerve cells were dying. Using a vivid war metaphor, she envisioned the maneuvers of large armies on a battlefield covered with corpses.[89]

The scenarios she came across impressed her deeply because they showed that the nervous system, far from being static, employed a radically different strategy from what she had envisioned up to that point. Ten to twenty hours later, the corpses would be removed by specially trained crews, and a few hours after that, scavenger cells known as macrophages would clean up the "battlefield" by devouring the remains of the dead neurons. To her astonishment, the same pattern was repeated slide after slide, clearly indicating that this specific part of the nervous system's development responded to a genetic program. The startling realization that nerve cell populations were subject to quotas, and to elimination of excess numbers, showed that there was a tenuous and yet valid path to follow into the intriguing and uncharted labyrinth of the nervous system.[90] In other words, at the embryonic stage, the leftover cells in the nervous system, which were not able to connect with the others and therefore survive, were automatically eliminated.

She was so excited that she asked Viktor Hamburger to quickly join her in the lab and showed him hundreds of slides and sketches she had drawn of what she had witnessed. He, too, was surprised and impressed, thinking that, thanks to her intuition and relentless dedication, she had found a new way of investigating the nervous system's development.

Rita decided to celebrate this important discovery by playing one of her favorite recordings she kept in the lab—"Air on the G string" (Suite No. 3 in D major, BWV 1068) by J. S. Bach— thus sealing, so to speak, a "lifelong alliance" between herself and the nervous system, an alliance she would never break. She had fully regained the faith in experimental neuroembryology that she thought was irreparably lost.

Her life among books, embryos, and music was all she wanted at that stage in her life, and when her work showed some promising progress, she even had glimpses of perfect happiness.

As she wrote to her mother and Paola, Rita smelled a stimulating "fragrance of truffles" in the air, and for the first time she was determined to capitalize on this specific discovery. Among the many scientific revolutions that were already in the making, her findings were innovative and noteworthy. She too could be the protagonist of an investigation providing a new and important way to understand the nervous system. It was a breakthrough that left a long-lasting mark on her. Even though the entire process of interpreting what she had witnessed together with Professor Hamburger on that special day had only taken about an hour, it took her over a year to rigorously reconstruct and explain the whole discovery in writing, in an article published in 1948.

Chapter Eight

THE DISCOVERY OF NERVE GROWTH FACTOR

What did Rita mean by the very Piedmontese metaphor "fragrance of truffles"? She actually did not know yet. It was only an intuition, but by then she had come to trust her sense of smell and the sudden intuitive leaps that would take her years of painstaking experiments to prove scientifically. She realized that she was on her way to finding the scent-trail of large specimens, but she did not know when and in what ground.

The answer came one morning in January 1950, when the temperature was -4 degrees Fahrenheit (-20 degrees Celsius) and the whole Washington University campus was buried in snow. Viktor Hamburger reached Rita in the lab and showed her a letter and an article written by his former student Elmer Bueker, then working in Washington, D.C., at Georgetown University. For almost two years, while in St. Louis, Bueker had been trying to find out how the development and differentiation of the chick embryo's nervous system were regulated. He was the first to transplant fragments of cancerous tumors onto embryos instead of grafting extra limbs onto them, but later decided to abandon that particular line of research.

Perhaps he had undervalued what he was investigating or was distracted by more pressing needs to support his family. Bueker had managed, however, to write a brief article on this original research, which was published in 1948, and asked Professor Hamburger for an opinion.[91] Rita immediately knew that she was confronting a supremely important message whose meaning had to be deciphered.

They both agreed to suspend their ongoing experiments and instead diligently repeat the ones Bueker described in detail in his article. With his approval, ten days later they received from the Jackson Memorial Institute a box full of small mice, carriers of a tumor called sarcoma 180, or S-180.

The ciphered message was soon revealed. With the very first experiments, Rita already had the feeling—which became more of a certainty over the following weeks—that she had come upon a phenomenon without precedent in the rich case history of experimental embryology.[92]

The effects of grafting S-180 were entirely different from those of limb buds and other embryonic tissues. Moreover, a second shipment from the same institute had been grafted with a tumor known as sarcoma 37 (S-37), offering further options for research. Both had been derived from mouse mammary carcinomas that had lost their original structure and had started to grow in a disordered and tumultuous way.

Rita had the sense of a curtain suddenly being opened. With

trepidation she started examining the chick embryos that were only eleven days old, eight days after the mouse tumors had been transplanted onto them. She thought she was hallucinating to begin with when she saw the nerve fibers growing profusely from the embryo, running everywhere among the tumor cells "like rivulets of water flowing over a bed of stones."[93] The new scientific scenario opening in front of her eyes was extraordinary. The first findings demonstrated that the tumor promoted an excessive growth with total disregard for the organism's requirements, altering the sequence of events that characterized normal developmental processes. The "truffles" she had been looking for with dogged persistence were precisely the two tumors S-180 and S-37 she was now experimenting with.

In a very affectionate letter dated March 1, 1951, Rita explained cancer to Paola as if she was trying to convey a biblical story in the simplest possible way. First of all, she pointed out that cancer is not an illness in the sense of a pathological process, but rather consists in the rebellion of one cell against the laws that regulate the development and vitality of the organism. "Where there is order, cancer brings chaos, marking the victory of anarchy over the law," Rita wrote. In *Abbi il coraggio di conoscere* (*Dare to Know*), which was published fifty years later, she dedicated a whole chapter to this topic, entitled "Is cancer an illness?"[94] By resorting to biblical analogies she presented the disease as a diabolical drama that upsets that ingrained sense of order that is at the base of the universe and of our lives as humans. In the case of cancer, the rebellious cell is always victorious. After having been obedient for so long—like Satan before rebelling against God—the tumor multiplies in a chaotic way without any relation whatsoever to the demands of the body. It no longer collaborates with the cells nearby, but aggressively destroys them. There is no resistance by the part attacked, only unconditional surrender, in a process that has no parallel.[95]

Rita deduced that the tumors she started grafting onto chick embryos must release some mysterious fluid that stimulates the growth and differentiation of nerves, in particular sympathetic nerves. The validity of this hypothesis, for her an intuitive certainty, was confirmed years later with a substantial number of in vivo and in vitro experiments. During the next few months she was totally absorbed by her experiments in search of conclusive evidence, aware that the new field of research that was opening ahead was in reality much vaster than she could possibly have imagined.[96] Although she was a secular scientist, Rita truly believed that science was connected with magic and wonder in its exploration of the mysteries of life and of the universe. Whenever she was looking through the microscope and recognized what she called the "miracle" of the humoral factor, her thoughts would inevitably go to the blood of San Gennaro, the patron saint of Naples, which unfailingly liquefied inside a sacred vial every year on September 19 in the presence of hundreds of pilgrims. This witty and endearing religious parallel highlighted Rita's almost devotional attitude toward her mission. According to Pietro Calissano, Rita, besides being gifted with a great intuitive capacity, had total, almost monastic dedication to her work.[97]

It was during one of those special, productive mornings of experimentation that the voice of Professor Giuseppe Levi boomed unexpectedly down the hallway of the Rebstock Hall building. Rita knew he was planning to visit the States, but she was not sure he could make it to St. Louis. After delightedly greeting her old mentor and briefing him on her experiments, she asked him to look through the microscope, expecting some kind of appreciation. Instead, he shook his "leonine mane"— still almost entirely red, though he was over eighty—and expressed only dismay, vigorously roaring as in the old times at the University of Turin. He was convinced that what he saw were not nerves but connective fibers. According to him, she had misread the results, and were she to persist in her convictions, she would definitely ruin her reputation.

Such cutting remarks from Professor Levi would have tormented her with self-doubt back in Turin, but now she was more confident. Rita was so convinced she was right that she steered Professor Levi away from any further discussion and convinced him instead to visit the Grand Canyon during his first trip to North America. She did not want to spend all her energy arguing with a mentor to whom she owed so much.

During the three days he was away, Rita diligently made drawings on paper of patterns of fibers she had seen under the microscope, but when she presented them to him, he was again extremely skeptical. He could not easily accept that "a tumor could change the way nerve fibers grow."

As soon as Levi left, Rita concentrated on a different but highly efficient experiment. Instead of transplanting the tumor tissue on the chick embryos themselves, she would graft the tissue onto the protective membrane—also known as the corioallantoic membrane—that grew around them. Each time, she would make a small hole in the egg's shell through which she could peer at the development of the transplanted fragments through her stereomicroscope. After about ten days of incubation, she would remove the embryos, properly salt-stained, and examine them carefully under the microscope. Each time she saw the same nerve growth that she had witnessed before, she became more and more convinced that the mysterious substance released by the tumor had to be a liquid.[98]

In January 1951, she wrote to Renato Dulbecco, who immediately assured her that the discovery was "a sensational event." Rita and Renato had become close friends and constantly consulted on major intuitions and findings. She also informed Rodolfo Amprino, who congratulated her warmly, showing his appreciation.

That was the year when Professor Hamburger decided that Rita deserved to be promoted to associate researcher for her dedication and ceaseless experimentation.

She presented her results at the 1951 New York Academy of Sciences symposium in a paper vaguely titled "The Chick Embryo in Biological Research." Paul Weiss, defining her paper as "the most exciting discovery of the year," must have been deploying his well-seasoned intuition, for it would be another three years before Rita's discovery was even given a name.[99]

Her 1950–51 experiments had indeed been exceptionally exciting and promising. By then she knew that by grafting the cancerous cells of male adult mice onto the embryo, the production of nervous fibers would be exponentially accelerated. However, was it really true that those cells contained a unique humoral substance able to increase growth? How could she identify that mysterious fluid? If she succeeded, Rita would certainly have made a sensational discovery that would also help to develop the treatment of many diseases of the nervous system.

The journey ahead was still very long and she was aware she was only taking her first steps. In order to address this issue, it was necessary to interrupt the usual time-consuming embryological experiments and instead conduct serious biological tests using the rigorous in vitro techniques she had learned at the University of Turin, still considered among the most reliable procedures available. Unfortunately, Washington University was not equipped for this kind of scientific verification. She knew that in Brazil—more specifically in Rio de Janeiro, at the Institute of Biophysics, directed by professor Carlos Chagas Filho—she would be able to successfully complete her research, especially since her friend Hertha Meyer, a former assistant of Professor Levi, was working there in a specialized lab she had set up in 1939. Thanks to Hamburger's encouragement and approval from the very start, Rita obtained a Rockefeller Foundation grant.

So, in September 1952, after a few days in Turin with her family, she flew to Rio de Janeiro, smuggling two tiny white mice bearing the tumors she wanted to test, tucked in a box inside a pocket of her overcoat. She was so pleased and excited to carry on her research for a few months in Brazil, a country she had always wanted to see. The fact that it lay some 4,971 miles (8,000 kilometers) away meant nothing compared to it being a place where she could count on access to suitable scientific equipment for the next step of her research. Moreover, the reservations expressed by her former mentor did not affect her secret certainty that she was finally on the right track.

She was welcomed at the airport by her friend Hertha, a German-Jewish scientist, who had also been a victim of racial persecution. When Hitler came to power, Professor Levi had invited Hertha to the University of Turin, where she spent six productive years until the start of the anti-Semitic campaign in Italy. She then wisely accepted the invitation of Carlos Chagas Filho to the University of Rio de Janeiro, to organize and direct in the laboratory of the Institute of Biophysics a specialized unit of in vitro culture, since she had learned it so proficiently at the universities of Berlin and Turin.

Rita was taken to the neighborhood of Copacabana, where arrangements were made for her to stay with some of Hertha's friends. She spent most of her days at the Institute of Biophysics, which was not far away from Praia Vermelha, a small beach under Sugarloaf Mountain, one of the most stunning sites in Brazil. Every morning Rita would reach the lab by *bonde*, similar to the Turin streetcars of her childhood. She would climb onto the footboard, because the carriages were so crowded that she would not even try to enter, and happily hung from the platform. Ticket sellers behaved like acrobats, leaping with agility from one footboard to the next, checking that every passenger had a ticket. Along with white-collar employees and workers going to offices and factories, there were many people wearing beach clogs, multicolored dresses, and swimsuits, clearly going to the seaside.

At the Institute of Biophysics, she was welcomed by Professor Chagas Filho, a well-known scientist in the field of neurophysiology. Still very young, he was friendly and keenly interested in Rita's research project.

After a number of negative tests from her experiments, Rita, instead of feeling depressed, trusted her own patience, a virtue she had cultivated since her student days, and resolved to try something different. She decided to grow embryo nerve tissue along with pieces of the tumor tissue in vitro, rather than reproduce the nerve growth by injecting extracts from the tumors into whole chick embryos. Tissue culture would also speed up her work, allowing her to see results not in weeks but in hours. It worked very well.

In those four intense months, she turned from keeping a diary to sending long, twice-weekly letters to Hamburger reporting her successes and failures, her ups and downs, since she had always considered herself "an artisan of research." In particular, she described and documented with many ink drawings the extraordinary dense halo-shaped outgrowth of nerve fibers stemming from the ganglia grown in proximity to the previously transplanted tumors. Most of the drawings of the halo effect were done on the margins of her letters, written on onionskin airmail paper in a compact handwriting that her family jokingly called *zampe di gallina* ("chicken scratch").

She was so enchanted by the contemplation of the beauty of

the thick halos of fibers she called "fibrillar, like the rays of the sun" that she never got tired of repeating the same experiments and documenting them with numerous India-ink drawings and detailed written reports. Her correspondence from September 1952 to the end of January 1953, fifty letters in all, was generously returned to her by Professor Hamburger in 1980 when he learned she intended to write her autobiography.

So many doubts came to her while she was in Rio. Was she searching in the right direction? Where was the proof that the in vitro effect, so different from that induced by grafting S-180 or S-37 in chick embryos, was provoked by the neoplastic cells releasing the same factor at work on the developing embryo? Since neoplastic cells replicate faster than normal ones, could the difference be only quantitative and, as such, be totally unrelated to the in vivo effects? Usually, after venturing a hypothesis derived from an experiment, a scientist carries out further experiments to replicate the findings; if they do not succeed, the hypothesis is changed. Rita's intuition told her that the nerve growth effect of the normal tissue and that of the tumor tissue were radically different, and she refused to abandon this idea. She decided, therefore, to simply disregard the facts that were in contrast with her envisioned hypothesis, by scrupulously following Russian neuropsychologist Alexander Luria's "law of disregard of negative information." This way she could single out and concentrate exclusively on the facts that would reinforce her rooted convictions.

In the last two months of her stay in Rio, her efforts in fact concentrated on her inner certainty that the effects of tumors

S-180 or S-37 induced in vitro were the result of the same agent that caused in vivo the precocious differentiation and increase in the overall volume of the ganglia in embryos.[100] Repeating the same experiments and growing the two tumor tissues together for several days instead of only one day, Rita finally obtained clear results. The side of the ganglia that was next to the tumor tissue showed much more intense nerve fiber growth than the side farther away, and the fibers seemed to be growing primarily toward the tumor.[101]

This seemed to confirm that the mysterious unidentified substance released by the neoplastic cells was stimulating their growth, showing a neurotrophic property, but also attracting nerve fibers toward its source and therefore had a neurotropic quality as well. On November 2, 1952, Rita wrote a euphoric letter to Hamburger about this finding that would be confirmed by larger-scale experiments performed in the following weeks. The data of these experiments were published in 1954 in the scientific journal *Cancer Research* and co-signed by Rita along with Hertha Meyer and Viktor Hamburger. She was able to go back to St. Louis in an optimistic state of mind and continue her investigations.

Rita left with the most positive impression of Rio, alive with singing and the rhythmic beating of drums, especially in proximity to the Carnival. In the month of January, people were joyful, kind, and hospitable, and already busy trying on their colorful costumes for the upcoming festival. She often compared Brazil to Italy, writing home that the sea in Rio was as blue as in Capri and that the beach of Copacabana reminded her of

Forte dei Marmi. She loved the sun and the beauty of the sea. Hertha, in an interview years later, observed how Rita bartered the primitive conditions of the lab for the beauty of the beaches of Rio, where she religiously went every day during the lunch break. She could not resist the beauty of the place, to the point that sometimes she would impulsively enter the sea fully dressed and then change at the institute. For Rita, beauty was an essential element both in nature and in the experiments she made in the lab. Beauty was the lymph of both life and scientific research and the two came to overlap. She was intrigued by the beauty of an organ as perfect as the brain, with its cells rich with secrets, and she was convinced that even the mysterious factor that stimulated the nerve cells to grow had its own intrinsic beauty.[102]

She could not stay for the annual Carnival, but she could instead join thousands of people, mostly Black men and women, attending the rites honoring Iemanjà, the goddess of the sea, brought to Brazil by West African slaves. Devotees, traditionally dressed in white, carried her statue to Copacabana beach, tossing flowers and other offerings into the sea. Rita was thrilled to see wealthy citizens and poor people from the favelas, or city slums, taking part side by side. A variety of races was also represented: white, Black, Native Indian, and a mixture of all three. Unlike Italy, Germany, and some Eastern European countries, transformed by racial discrimination into prison camps for years— or the Florida she had recently visited, where there was a rigid apartheid—Rio delighted in producing a harmonious swirling crowd, speaking different languages and dialects. She was so touched the night she spent by the ocean among thousands of people with torches that she, too, "lit a candle" in her mind to honor that marvelous crucible of different races in a spirit of true multiculturalism.[103]

Her stay in Brazil and her experience of the preparations for Carnival even affected her approach to the growth factor she was trying so hard to identify, because at some point it appeared to her as a vision of a masked figure in the crowd. An amazing metamorphosis! That same X factor that had appeared in vitro for the first time in St. Louis revealed itself to her in a "theatrical and grandiose way," as if spurred by the bright atmosphere of the explosive and exuberant manifestation of life that is the Carnival in Rio.[104] From that moment on for Rita, the mysterious X factor became a creature of its own, gradually developing an independent life.

Before returning to Washington University, she enriched her traveling experience by visiting Quito, the capital of Ecuador, which, according to Rita, was the most ancient and richest colonial center of South America. She was excited to be going back to her research in St. Louis, but she knew she could not further identify the nerve growth factor released by mouse sarcomas all by herself. She needed the help of a biochemist.

In late January 1953, she was delighted, in spite of the chilly Midwest wind, to be welcomed home at the airport of St. Louis not only by Professor Hamburger, but also by Stanley Cohen. He was a young, qualified biochemist who had just been hired, as she had been previously informed in a letter while in Rio. After her exciting experience in Brazil she was tanned and beaming with joy, looking much younger than her age of forty-four, and she could not believe how enthusiastically her return was celebrated by students and colleagues, including her new research associate.

Stanley, or Stan, as he introduced himself to the team, was about thirty; he had a wife and two children, a dog, a pipe always in his mouth, very little care for his appearance, and a passion for the flute. Above all, he was an excellent biochemist, highly competent and intuitive, as well as extremely modest. His main task was to identify the chemical nature of the growth-promoting substance that Rita had discovered. They soon realized they had a lot to learn from each other. Rita knew very little about biochemistry and Cohen was not familiar at all with the nervous system. She knew that the "fibrillar halo," which grew around sensory and sympathetic ganglia in the proximity of mouse sarcoma fragments S-180 and S-37, was the philosopher's stone to explain the unidentified nature of the mysterious factor released by the tumors. Upon her return, she immediately set up an in vitro tissue culture unit in her lab, similar to the one she had in Rio, to confirm the results she had obtained in Brazil, and Stan proved to be the ideal colleague.

Born of Russian Jewish immigrants, Stan completed a degree in zoology from Oberlin College in Ohio in 1945, a doctorate in biochemistry from the University of Michigan, and a post-doctoral fellowship at Washington University with Professor Martin Kamen, a well-known chemist. He was happy to accept the position of research associate from Professor Hamburger. From that winter day in 1953 to the summer of 1959, he and Rita met many times a day, either in his lab on the ground floor of Rebstock Hall or in hers on the second floor, to share information, brainstorm together, and witness with trepidation the gradual identification of that key substance—or mysterious character—who first appeared in Rio. Professor Hamburger constantly followed the exciting results of their experiments and encouraged their persistent, enlightened joint research.

Rita admired Stan's positive attitude toward other people and their research. He had an inadequate opinion of himself. He modestly thought he could solve problems only by hard work. He never paraded the chemical expertise and intuition that underlay his everyday dedication. It had truly been a lucky star that brought them together because their skills complemented each other in working toward their common objective. While he respected Rita's intuitive leaps, she appreciated Stan's one-step-at-a-time approach. She felt she spent the six most productive years of her life working by his side. Every day he would come, limping slightly, to the lab from his cottage nearby, along with Smog, his sweet mongrel dog who would lie down quietly while Stan sat at his desk, pipe in mouth. Smog also kept "a loving eye" on his master while Stan was playing the flute, in rare moments of relaxation.

After a year of research, Stan identified the tumoral factor as a nucleoprotein, a combination of nucleic acid and protein. In 1954, this macromolecule was named by both of them, with trepidation and almost incredulity, as nerve growth factor (NGF). It also sounded good in Italian: *fattore di crescita nervosa*. Stan's saying, "You and I are good, but together we are wonderful," remained emblematic of the kind of enthusiasm and constructive atmosphere they created at Rebstock Hall. Thirty-five years later, in 1986, when they shared the Nobel Prize for this discovery, they happily repeated this statement to each other, more convincingly than ever.

Still to be determined, however, was the question of which part was biologically active: the proteic, the nucleic, or both? At this point Stan had to analyze further and, advised by fellow biochemist Arthur Kornberg, another future Nobel Prize winner, used for the first time the venom of a poisonous snake, the water moccasin, which, in small quantities, was used in the treatment of snake bites. One spring day in 1956, Stan gave Rita a venom-treated sample, along with others, without specifying which was which, so that she could not prejudge any of the results. It turned out that one of the samples produced "a stupendous halo"—in other words, far more nerve growth than the others. At this point they added a little purified snake venom to one of Rita's nerve tissue cultures. The result was a tremendous amount of nerve growth. The active component, therefore, was the protein part of the "wonder" macromolecule.

The discovery was astounding and multileveled. First of all, they had come across a new, totally unhoped-for source of NGF: The snake venom was a thousand times richer than the substance of the tumor tissues. This also meant that NGF was indeed a protein, since nucleic acid could not survive in the venom.

Over the next two years, from 1956 to 1958, Stan was also able to specify in detail the chemical nature of the protein and its molecular weight. By repeating experiments over and over, they were able to identify and isolate in one protein molecule the factor that caused the growth and differentiation of the cells of the nervous system. They both worked frantically, often even after dinner and on Sundays.

They had a little zoo of over thirty turtles, ten alligators, eight white rabbits, over a hundred rats and mice, seven cats, and more than ten kittens to look after. Rita, in particular, felt responsible and was happy to feed the animals necessary for the ongoing experiments with fresh milk, meat, and vegetables when their assistants were not there.

To reach their objectives, Rita decided they must visit the National Cancer Institute, one of the most important scientific institutions in the US, a few miles from Washington, DC, in Bethesda, Maryland. After a few days they both came back with plenty of useful information to intensify their research.

In a 1958 paper, Rita was in a position to give "irrefutable evidence" that the nerve growth factor could be extracted not only from mouse cancer tissues, but also from snake venom, and the effects were the same both in vitro and in vivo. This paper contributed to her promotion to full professor that year but did not stop the two future Nobel winners from persisting in their research. They soon discovered that male mice salivary glands make a mild poison that the mice inject when they bite. This compound was similar to snake venom in weakening opponents of the same species, especially when fighting over females. In no time they realized, with a mixture of happiness and surprise, that the mouse salivary gland extracts produced nerve growth with "fibrillar" halos greater than any Rita and Stan had seen before.[105] Later on, Stan determined that this also promoted the growth of skin and accelerated the growth of teeth in newborn mice. Research on the effects of NGF was gradually also extended to other species.

Rita and Stan presented this new scientific data at an international congress in Baltimore in 1959. Yet because their discoveries did not fit any pre-existing conceptual schemes, they received a lukewarm, if not skeptical, reception. All the same, this series of extraordinary findings marked a revolution in the field of neuroscience, as Viktor Hamburger immediately realized.

Who could ever have imagined? It all started with a few eggs, a needle, and the relentless curiosity of a stubborn girl. Chance and good luck also played a significant part. It was like fortuitously discovering "a cave of precious stones while hiking up a hill on a trail that is not expected to bring one anywhere but to the top of the hill."[106] Each of their discoveries, however, did not mark a point of arrival, but rather a step toward a new departure.

On June 11, 1959, just one month before Stan's acceptance of a new academic post in Tennessee—due to Washington University's lack of funding—Rita and her research associate made another most exciting co-discovery. This marked a "memorable event in neuroembryology," according to Viktor Hamburger, who stopped by Rita's lab that day, saying: "Remember the date of this finding!" They had decided to run their experiments in reverse and discovered, to their great surprise, that NGF was not only a factor that could produce an odd stimulation of nerve growth, but also inhibit it. Having observed that snake venom antiserum could slow down nerve growth, Stan concocted an antiserum specific to salivary NGF and made experiments with it to find out that, indeed, it inhibited nerve growth. On her side, Rita injected it into newborn rats to discover that, once more, the size of some nerve growth had decreased.[107] Strikingly, they found that treatment with this antiserum almost completely abolished sympathetic nerve development, comparable to the phenotype that resulted from ablating the wing buds in chick embryos. Both Stanley and Rita found these results promising.

Professor Hamburger understood immediately that this was a historical breakthrough. Rita had proven once more to be a real asset for the university, but her battle was not easy because her finding defied any given canon of neurobiological research, which then was based on the belief that the nervous system was rigidly planned in every component and, as such, could not be modified by any external developing factor. Only about twenty years later was NGF fully understood in its wide spectrum of interactive biological functions in the nervous, endocrine, and immune systems.

Rita was now coming to the end of one of her most prodigiously productive stages of scientific research when Stan, with his magical intuition and flute, played the part of the wizard, charming snakes at will and getting the miraculous fluid to flow forth from the minuscule mouths of mice.[108]

The long saga of the nerve growth factor, however, had only just begun.

Chapter Nine

COMMUTING BETWEEN THE USA AND ITALY

Rita's anxiety at facing a future of research without the precious help of Stanley Cohen, now based at Vanderbilt University School of Medicine in Nashville, was soon alleviated by meeting Pietro Angeletti, a young researcher with a degree in medicine from the University of Perugia. He had just joined Washington University Medical School to pursue studies in neuroscience. Throughout her career, Rita constantly preferred to work with gifted colleagues rather than alone. She firmly believed in interaction and in reciprocal enrichment through stimulating debate. On her own initiative she sought out Angeletti in the lab of the Department of Pathology, where she found him totally absorbed at the microscope. He knew about her field of research and had hoped to meet her. It was the autumn of 1960 and their encounter marked the beginning of a fruitful collaboration that continued, uninterrupted, for twelve years, in the US and later in Italy. He was soon able to take over Stan's engagement in the biochemical investigation of NGF.

They both wanted to go back to Italy, at least part of the time, so she conceived a project that she could have not realized without him. Once again, she was blessed by her lucky star. In a letter to her family, she praised Pietro (whom everybody called Piero) and compared him to Renato Dulbecco because he was very orderly, precise, intelligent, and quick-witted. "Working with him is like being on a treadmill," Rita said.

She was now regularly invited to major conferences, along with Dulbecco and Luria, and was admired for her competence, elegance, and eloquence. Yet ultimately she still felt like an immigrant, compelled to stay in the US for professional and economic reasons. Her state-of-the-art lab and her welcoming and comfortable new apartment were no longer enough; she found that she was suffering from an incurable nostalgia for her country, family, and friends.

Rita was very grateful to have been given the possibility of building her whole academic career in St. Louis. After having been promoted to associate professor in 1956, she was now an American citizen and a full professor of neurobiology, and intended to honor that position by remaining at Washington University until her retirement in 1977. She had been offered other academic options at Purdue University in Indiana and at the National Institutes of Health in Puerto Rico. However, she preferred to stay at Washington University because of her strong connection with Professor Hamburger, who had always encouraged her in all the different stages of her research and granted her an unprecedented professional freedom. She was allowed to participate at any congress she had been invited to, as well as spend four months in Brazil at the Institute of Biophysics in Rio.

She also stayed three months in California to teach at Caltech in Pasadena. There, thanks to Renato Dulbecco, she had the good fortune of meeting Max Delbrück, who shared the Nobel Prize with Salvador Luria in 1969. The freedom she experienced enriched her scientifically and culturally. Along with Delbrück, his wife, and Dulbecco, she was invited to hike in unique places such as Death Valley, California, and the canyons of Arizona, spending nights scrutinizing the sky with a telescope while camping or sleeping under the stars. They all became close friends, also sharing evenings together in Los Angeles, attending concerts. A particularly memorable one was conducted by Igor Stravinsky himself. In her correspondence to her mother and Paola, Rita was very excited and described the seventy-five-year-old composer leading the orchestra from the podium as having the agility of a "grass-hopper."

Rita's sense of appreciation and loyalty to Hamburger as chair of her department was also due to all the privileges that she gradually acquired. Thanks to her status of full professor, Rita had been able to count on close collaborators such as Martha Fuhrmann, the efficient administrative coordinator, and above all, her research associate and dear friend Fernando J., nicknamed Nando. Tragically he had died prematurely. She would dedicate a whole chapter in her autobiography to him. Inevitably, however, she started thinking of her future.

Now that she was a mature woman and an acclaimed

scientist, heading her own lab at Rebstock Hall, would she want to spend the rest of her life in the marvelous isolation offered her by the Midwest?[109] After almost fifteen years in North America, she felt a strong desire to be closer to her family. For all this time she had been "*la zia d'America*" ("the American aunt"), sending presents home to nephews and nieces, far away from her native city and deep emotional ties.

In Italy there was her elderly mother, Adele, and Rita's twin, who, out of modesty, wrote about everybody except herself in her letters. By 1960, however, Paola had earned recognition and respect as an important Italian painter, engraver, and sculptor. There was her brother, Gino, an architect and sculptor, whom she trusted and admired so much. His children, Piera and Emanuele, would often write to Rita, asking for advice, and she replied with a number of letters, later published in *Cantico di una vita*.

Then there was Nina, the eldest sister. In 1959, she had tragically lost her son Guido, a vulnerable and sensitive twenty-six-year-old. The death of Rita's nephew left an indelible mark on her. It was a mysterious death, alone in Trana, a little town in the mountains near Turin, that according to Rita actually came "as a relief, a liberation" he was secretly aspiring to. Having spent some time with him during the summer holidays, Rita had realized that his health was precarious, but had not understood how irreparably compromised his mental condition really was. She paid tribute to him in "*Consummatum est*," the moving first chapter of *Senz'olio contro vento*, a personal collection of portraits of people she cherished, who led their lives with great difficulty, "against the wind."[110] She wrote many letters to her family with the intention of consoling Nina in particular, trying to explain the reasons for Guido's death in scientific terms, yet she suffered very much. It was through intense work that she finally managed to overcome her grief and sense of loss.

The success of the experiments she performed in the US was such that her return to Italy, at least for a few months a year, became a real possibility. Rita was becoming popular, a sort of charismatic scientific star featured in a major article in the *New York Herald Tribune* and in scientific journals. She was especially appreciated by the Italian community of St. Louis as an important compatriot; they proudly called her "la Professoressa italiana." She was teaching, researching, writing, and traveling from one conference to the next to prove the validity of her findings.

Gone were the days when she had reached the States with Renato Dulbecco by ship in two weeks. She now traveled constantly by plane, which made her journeys quick and easy. She held fast to her secret dream of acting as a bridge between her home country, which had shaped her, and the one that had welcomed her and allowed her to become an internationally recognized scientist. She therefore developed the idea of establishing a small research unit in Italy that would collaborate with Washington University. In the early sixties, Italy itself was becoming a center of scientific excellence. In the field of biomedicine, its Advanced Institute of Health (*Istituto Superiore di Sanità*, or ISS) was an example to the world, and its faculty included two Nobel Prize winners: Daniel Bovet from Switzerland, and the German-British Ernst Chain, who, along with

Alexander Fleming and Howard Florey, had been awarded the Nobel Prize in Medicine or Physiology for discovering penicillin.

Rita presented her project to Viktor Hamburger, who proved to be understanding, and in turn consulted with the medical school's dean, who authorized Rita to spend a few months each year in Italy to establish the new unit. This became possible thanks to the instrumental support of her new collaborator, Piero Angeletti, who would direct the laboratory in the United States during the trimester she would be researching in Italy. Rita also won a grant for this special innovative program from the National Science Foundation, a US federal government funding agency, and by the spring of 1961 she was ready to leave for Italy.[111]

Rita's goal was to create a center of excellence giving space and opportunities to young talents to dedicate themselves to scientific research, without having to pay the high price of emigrating, as she had done. But in which city should she create this pioneering institution? Her heart was inclined to choose Turin. That same year, Italy was celebrating the one hundredth anniversary of its unity, and the young Queen Elizabeth II had inaugurated the British Pavilion in Rita's hometown, in the presence of an international audience. However, Rita soon realized that Rome was a more logical and natural choice. She was accustomed by now to let reason prevail over emotions and allow collective interests to take precedence over personal ones.

In a letter to her family, she wrote: "Just as Columbus discovered America I am ready to discover Rome."

The same country that had expelled her from the university

at the time of the racial laws now welcomed her with all honors, and with some additional funding from the National Research Council (*Consiglio Nazionale delle Ricerche*, or CNR), which would later invite her to direct the Research Center for Neurobiology. She first obtained equipment and laboratory space in the basement of the *Istituto Superiore di Sanità*. Soon, thanks to Professor G. B. Marini-Bettòlo, director of the biochemistry department and collaborator of Nobel Prize winner Daniel Bovet, Rita's research quarters in Rome had become larger than those at Washington University: three spacious rooms fully equipped with all the instruments necessary for structural, ultra-structural, and biochemical research. She would recruit in no time an excellent team of young scientists to further research the implications of NGF. Most of the researchers she employed accepted a modest remuneration—with the incentive of possibly moving with Rita to Washington University for a few months over the next fifteen years until her retirement from her American university.

Rita started her new life as a commuter between two continents with all the advantages and disadvantages of such a challenge. She had to loosen her close ties with colleagues and friends in the Midwest, in particular Viktor Hamburger, with whom she had by then forged a solid bond of friendship. She had to become a sort of wonder woman, coordinating two laboratories thousands of miles apart, working on a discontinuous basis. Fortunately her colleague Piero Angeletti shared the same aspiration of dividing time and responsibilities between the two countries. Moreover, in St. Louis, Rita could count on the invaluable help of an administrative coordinator, while at the new center in Rome, she had to look after the administration and the archives herself. A heavy workload for a scientific globe-trotter! She had the feeling of becoming a pioneer again—but this time in her home country.

She gradually began to stay longer in Italy, and this luxury allowed her the great joy of spending every weekend with her mother in the last two years of her life. During the racial perse-cutions, Rita had been anguished at the idea that her mother would end up in Nazi hands. After the war, Adele had shown great endurance as the years passed, encouraging her daughter to pursue her life of research across the ocean. Every time Rita would leave for the States, after a brief holiday, Adele would urge her to face their separation in a serene way. She never mentioned the serious attacks of asthma that had started afflicting her in 1963. Their mutual love was expressed silently rather than with words, and had grown deeper through the years.

When Rita came back to Italy in the summer of 1963, she found her mother in a wheelchair, with a fractured thigh bone. Unfortunately, that apparently minor accident proved to be the beginning of the end. When Rita arrived at the hospital in Turin, her dying mother reminded Rita of a saint on a fourteenth-century sarcophagus, and she felt as if the thread of her own life had also been cut.[112] Adele's last resting place was the ivory-colored granite tomb designed by Gino, where Rita's father had been lying, after a turbulent life, for thirty-two years.[113] It was to Adele and Paola that Rita had constantly written about her joys and disappointments, her aspirations and frustrations, reinforcing a true bond of loving and caring over the years.

Though the death of her mother increased Rita's real estate and land assets in Piedmont and Puglia, which she generously shared with her brother and her sister Paola, Rita was not particularly interested in accumulating wealth. She considered money more than anything else a useful tool for facilitating her research. As it happened, she had also been granted over $100,000 from the Hartford Foundation in New York for her discoveries, which greatly increased the prestige of the university in St. Louis, but gave rise to a degree of envy among her colleagues.

After Adele's death, Rita invited Paola to live with her in Rome, in a large apartment on the top floor of a building she bought in Viale di Villa Massimo, in the Quartiere Trieste, not too far from where she was working. There Paola could have her studio as well, in a separate adjacent flat. Paola agreed, and transformed the space into a work of art, creating a spectacular mosaic in black and white on the floor of the wide terrace in front of the living room. The mosaic drew the viewer into a universe where different planets turned on themselves in a cosmic dance, suggesting a kinetic portrait of two lives swirling with different rhythms, but converging toward the same harmony. Every window afforded a view of rose bushes and the centuries-old trees of Villa Torlonia, where Mussolini lived for almost twenty years.

Their domestic partnership enabled Rita to rediscover Paola's extraordinary sensibility, sense of privacy, and temperament, which through the years had become increasingly more intro-verted. Interestingly, the two sisters shared a similar gift for scouting young talents whom others had failed to notice. Rita, too, had an ability to detect promising young scientists, and in Italy, having become an institutional figure, she was able to support them.

She enjoyed Paola's company immensely while going to galleries and museums in Italy and other European countries. Through the years there was an increasing identification and bond between the two of them. They had both reached the peak of self-expression in their respective artistic and scientific fields by striving constantly for perfection and giving the best of themselves.

In spite of their different choices and opposite rhythms of life, they had both opted to dedicate themselves fully to their true vocations, which left little space or energy for raising fami-lies of their own. They both had remarkable mentors. Paola, since adolescence, had worked in the studio of Felice Casorati, a leading Italian artist who left a mark similar to the one Giuseppe Levi left on Rita. Having mentors did not prevent the twins from pursuing their own quests for identity. Rita rejoiced that Paola had been recognized by critics such as Gillo Dorfles and Giulio Carlo Argan, or by great artists like Giorgio de Chirico, who compared some of Paola's works to those of El Greco and Delac-roix. She was so proud of Paola, featured at the Musée du Jeu de Paume in Paris and at the Venice Biennale, that she constantly promoted her to friends and colleagues stating that she was one of "the best woman artists of the century." Thanks partly to Rita's support, Paola's works are now in major museums such as the Galleria Nazionale d'Arte Moderna e Contemporanea in Rome, Museo d'Arte Moderna e Contemporanea di Trento e Rovereto (MART), and the Jewish Museum in New York.

Like Rita in the field of neuroscience, Paola had constantly experimented. When Rita returned to Italy, her twin sister was engaged not only in paintings, but also in kinetic luminous sculptures that would architecturally "rise from the floor like stalactites"—fittingly for the sister of an architect—and large copper and stainless-steel engravings enriched with mysterious archaic alphabets and algebraic symbols, thus achieving a complexity that Rita described as "interplanetary." The sisters had parallel but complementary careers, one in the arts and one in the sciences, nonetheless originating from the same cerebral mechanisms. Paola, however, was creating her artwork in solitude while Rita's field required teamwork and interaction.

The sixties were years of changes and painful losses. In late January 1965, Rita surprised Professor Levi by paying him an unexpected visit at San Giovanni Hospital in Turin, where he had just been diagnosed with a malignant tumor. He was completely alone in his room, and through the window, she could see a mellow winter sunset. He was ninety-two and knew, with detachment and lucidity, exactly what he suffered from, well aware he would die in a few weeks.

He had always organized his life to be orderly and productive, starting his daily work at seven in the morning and ending late in the evening, except during his summer holidays in the mountains with his son Gino, where they would embark on invigorating excursions. At eighty-five his left leg had been amputated for circulatory deficiency. He showed his usual tenacity by learning how to walk again with an artificial leg and nothing would stop him from attending key meetings in Rome or traveling with his wife, Lidia, to the Swiss Alps. He was still young in mind and full of interests.

After Lidia's death, he knew he had reached the end of his journey. He still embodied great physical and moral strength; during the three full hours of his last "briefing" with Rita, he instructed her not to cry, but instead to detail the progress of her latest scientific endeavors, an account to which he listened with unflagging interest. He congratulated her on her expanding research, conceding that she had acquired all the elements to succeed. After so many years and under such different circumstances, they still were master and disciple.

Since nobody came to disturb them, Rita had the opportunity of reminiscing with him about her early days at the university, when she had failed to unravel cerebral convolutions in the brain of human fetuses. They also recalled the racial persecutions, and their humiliating dismissal from the University of Turin. While squeezing her hand energetically, Professor Levi remembered their stay in Belgium, their research in hiding in Turin in the small home lab, and their good fortune at meeting again in Florence during the Nazi occupation. They also talked of Rodolfo Amprino, his favorite student, as well as Salvador Luria and Renato Dulbecco, who had distinguished themselves, along with Rita, as the illustrious Italian trio in the USA. Before kissing her goodbye, he revealed what he believed to be his greatest secret: The deep influence he exerted on young people came from "the passion with which he had pursued his own studies and later directed those of his pupils," while remaining indifferent to any honor.

He died without knowing that three of his disciples would be awarded a Nobel Prize: Salvador Luria (1969), Renato Dulbecco (1975), and Rita (1986). And unbelievable as it may seem, from the labs of these three scientists, eight more Nobel Prizes followed.

Once back in St. Louis, Rita learned that Levi had passed away, just as he had foreseen; she could not help but think of the great likenesses between her master and her father, both gifted with extraordinary personalities. Despite some differences, they had the same resolute and imperious way of dealing with people and problems, the same energy that knew no obstacles to the realization of their work projects, and the same intolerance for superficiality and for the failure to perform duties. Rita proudly recognized that Professor Levi had accepted his destiny with a stoic serenity while maintaining till the very last an interest in research as an instrument for the understanding of nature and not as an object of competition and an instrument of power.[114] She humbly acknowledged that without him and his rigorous teaching, she would never have reached so many of her goals.

While in Rome she had become very aware that the discovery of NGF had shaken the existing neuroscience dogma, because it clearly indicated that the development of the nerve cells was not rigidly programmed from a genetic point of view, but responded to external factors.[115] As she admitted on more than one occasion, she initially had not grasped the full range of her finding, but having lived through the tragic experience of the Nazi persecutions, she declared she was very satisfied because "she was against every dogma."

Many aspects of NGF still had to be clarified, studied, and researched in depth. In spite of two major articles that Rita and Stanley Cohen had published in 1960 in the *Proceedings of the National Academy of Sciences* that highlighted their groundbreaking new findings, it was still like working in a sort of private hunting ground where few scientists ventured because the results were "so perplexing and hard to reconcile with prevailing theory."[116] Rita had also organized a conference on nerve growth factor to share her new discoveries, providing an opportunity for a number of scientists to bring forward new approaches and to branch out in different directions. She thought: Does NGF have the potential to help humankind? This discovery was indeed momentous and further exploration was certainly needed. She knew that it would take years, not months, to fully unravel the complexities.

Rita intended to replicate in Rome what she had previously done in the US with Stanley Cohen and then with Piero Angeletti. In order to pursue this project, she urgently needed a biochemist. Rita met Pietro Calissano, a twenty-seven-year-old graduate from the University of Genoa, in June 1965, after he had contacted her. She reached him in front of the Termini railway station, where he had just arrived. The fact that she offered to pick him up in an old Ford that she drove herself—never changing gears because she was accustomed to her American car—was a very unusual gesture in Italy, a country where professors, especially those already well known in the scientific world, were still regarded with great deference, as almost unapproachable authorities. She was a very unusual academic, always elegantly dressed, fragile-looking but perfectly matching the description given by Primo Levi of "a tiny lady with an indomitable will and the bearing of a princess." In Calissano's book *Rita Levi-Montalcini: La vita fra i neuroni* (*Life Among Neurons*), the author describes in detail their first encounter, which marked the beginning of a working relationship and friendship lasting half a century.

In her small Roman office at the Istituto Superiore di Sanità, she kept behind her desk a very visible quote by Albert Einstein: "Imagination is more important than knowledge." Rita stated on several occasions that she felt more artist than scientist. She was convinced she owed more to the right hemisphere of the brain than to the left, insofar as the left hemisphere is more analytical, verbal, and linear while the right one is synthetic, holistic, and in control of the musical and visual functions. Her greatest guide was always her infallible intuition, which, along with her unbridled imagination, formed "a unique cocktail" favoring her highly experimental approach to science.

She offered Calissano a fellowship in a very practical, matter-of-fact, American way. She initially proposed $100 a month, which was more than enough for him at that time (corresponding today to approximately $1,500). When she saw that he did not respond right away, however—he was actually thinking how to combine his private life in Genoa with his new position in Rome—she doubled her offer.[117] His task would be to investigate the NGF's mechanism of action. Working early every morning with Rita herself, he was struck by her capacity to give space to imagination and to consider the most daring proposals, provided they could be verified scientifically. He, too, was soon invited to spend an academic year at Washington University to properly combine efforts and reinforce close ties with the new center in Rome. So at this point there were two efficient groups dedicated to the investigation of NGF.

Living in Italy brought out, much more than before, another side of Rita's personality. She was an unusually stylish type of professor, often wearing a mink coat in winter and dresses with matching silk or brocade jackets, made specially for her by a couturier in Turin. Her old friend Salvador Luria wrote in his autobiography, *A Slot Machine, a Broken Test Tube*, that Rita was nicknamed "The Queen" not only because of her "regal manner," but also because of the impeccable dresses that she would wear in the lab with a standard white coat over them.[118] Her style of dressing became a way of communicating her personality. She herself designed her clothes to be inimitable, unique, always adorned with jewels, and defying the usual clichés about women scientists.

She had even restyled her hair from a bun to what author Sharon McGrayne described as a dramatic swoop.[119] For all her rather aristocratic aura, she did not care for the rigid formality that traditionally existed in relations between students and their superiors in Italy. In St. Louis she was accustomed to be addressed with an informal "Hi Doc." Students breathed a very stimulating atmosphere with her around, and were encouraged to interact with a highly intelligent, unconventional, and open-minded scientist. If Rita was a public icon, in her private life she was a very simple woman with a strong sense of humor who loved the everyday dimension of her work. She was particularly supportive of young people: From 1963 to 1969 she could count on the collaboration of Vincenzo Bocchini, an able young Neapolitan chemist, who helped Rita to overcome all kinds of increasing difficulties due to excessive Italian bureaucracy and a persistent lack of funds. After six years of working with great calm and competence for the Italian NGF group, he was eventually able to perfect the chemical procedures needed to extract pure chemical nerve growth factor.

She also started a unique lifelong collaboration with Luigi Aloe, a talented young technician from Perugia University and son of a Calabrian fisherman, who gradually became an indispensable investigator in the study of insects in relation to NGF. She came to appreciate his dedication, tenacity, and total availability to the point that she changed his life by fulfilling his dreams and thirst for knowledge. In 1968 they met in Rome at the Istituto Superiore di Sanità and she hired him as a lab technician and "guardian of cockroaches" to start new research at Washington University.[120]

She entered his life as "a hurricane," ultimately transforming him into a capable scientist (she jokingly called him "the first scientist of Amantea," his native town). She was sure that invertebrates produced a growth factor, and Luigi pursued this formidable idea, studying and experimenting at night in the lab, confirming her infallible intuition. In January 1972, this extraordinary discovery was published in an article in the *Journal of Neurobiology*, cosigned by teacher and student. Rita acknowledged his "green thumb," his outstanding skill in cultivating cells, which increasingly paved the way to other major findings that earned him an honorary degree in biology from the University of Bologna in 1989.

Rita also kept in touch with the scientists she trusted. She was delighted to host Stanley Cohen during his sabbatical in 1964. He had come to Rome and worked at her neurobiology center on the tissue culture of epidermal growth factor, which he had discovered back at Washington University.

In those years she felt at her best, an intercontinental commuter; she had become a real scientific ambassador between the old and the new continent. In a way she could be compared to the spectacular Gateway Arch that Eero Saarinen had designed for St. Louis, a landmark internationally appreciated as a powerful symbol of bridge-building and cultural growth.

The year 1969 stands out as a very important date for several reasons. Rita's small Center of Neurobiology was enlarged and transformed into an official organ of the National Research Council (CNR) that became known as the Laboratory of Cell Biology, thanks to Professor Vincenzo Caglioti, president of CNR. It was organized into four departments. Besides neurobiology, the new lab directed by Rita included cell biology, immunology, and mechanisms of gene expression. In her office a different quote appeared behind her desk, this time by Martin Luther King Jr.: "A man who does not have something for which he is willing to die is not fit to live." A meaningful motto indeed for a researcher who believed that science should be at the service of humanity.

That same year, Viktor Hamburger retired from Washington University, while Salvador Luria was awarded the Nobel Prize in Physiology or Medicine with two other protagonists of the Phage Group, Max Delbrück and Alfred Hershey. Luria, the leader of the brilliant Italian trio who landed in the US along with Rita and Renato, was the generous scientist who facilitated their future success to the point that the three of them became recognized as "the rock stars of science," unexpectedly attracting large crowds of admirers and wide press coverage. They were an honor to Italy and in particular to the University of Turin, their alma mater.

Rita's Roman office was re-established in a residential building near Piazza del Popolo. The change of address was not very successful. It created a number of issues such as the chaotic traffic in that particular area, a limited timetable for access to the building, and the settled dislike, on the part of the palazzo's owners, of the radioactive materials used in the lab. There were no security guards as at Washington University, which had enabled researchers to come and go at any hour of the day or night. Moreover, from the second half of the sixties to the beginning of the eighties, neurobiology in Italy was still considered a kind of Cinderella among the biological disciplines, "a sort of private hunting ground."[121] It was neglected even by CNR. Meanwhile, NGF studies were soaring in other countries, where perfectly equipped laboratories attracted young people to experiment in large, well-organized teams.

Rita's name had progressively disappeared from key publications on the finding of NGF and this phenomenon mysteriously lasted for quite some time. She was so disappointed that she stated in an interview for *Omni* magazine: "For a long time people didn't mention how NGF was discovered. My name was entirely left out of the literature . . . I am not a person to be bitter, but it was astonishing to find it completely cancelled."

Unfortunately, researchers in an institution like CNR were never monitored or checked, and preferred to work on an individual basis rather than in a team. There was a great deal of autonomy, with some interesting exceptions, because in this total freedom, creativity could eventually be expressed on rare occasion. Yet the growing frustration of the Italian research group, who were coping with the increasing lack of funding, led many of Rita's team members to seek work elsewhere. This complex and problematic scenario often provoked doubt in Rita as to whether to continue or desist.

Moreover, she had originally planned to share the directorship of the Laboratory of Cell Biology with Piero Angeletti, who had collaborated to arrange funding for the new institute, but the scarce attention Italy devoted to scientific research at that time led him to accept a financially rewarding offer from the American multinational pharmaceutical company Merck Sharp & Dohme, as director of chemical and pharmacological research. His friendship with Rita did not survive this hurtful blow. In fact, it would have been all but impossible for the study of nerve growth factor to continue in Italy had it not been for Rita's excellent collaborators and friends Pietro Calissano and

Luigi Aloe. Thanks to both of them, she managed to overcome moments of intense discouragement.

For over two decades beginning in the early 1960s, Calissano kept studying the mechanism of action in nerve growth factor along with two researchers on the Washington University team, Ralph Bradshaw and Ruth A. Hogue. Bradshaw and Hogue obtained pure samples of NGF and worked out the whole sequence that led to the identification in 1971 of the protein as a relatively small molecule, consisting of two identical chains, each 118 amino acids long.

Rita, along with Aloe, investigated the spectrum of action of that special molecule from a biological point of view. From the very beginning she had admired his scientific intuition and together the two of them managed to chart new territories, especially from 1969 to 1972, when she expanded her research from the NGF of the vertebrates to a possible GF of the invertebrates, turning to the study of the nervous system of insects.

Though Rita's work with cockroaches developed an entirely new field of research in neuroscience, she gradually realized that she could not give up her first love, her "child," to which she had dedicated most of her academic life. She decided once and for all to return to the study of NGF. It was her wisest decision. No regrets, no second thoughts. On the whole, she could count on a research group, which, with its quiet atmosphere of tenacious inquiry, reminded her of a small enclave of determined and persevering pioneers. She was also able to communicate to others her artisanal touch, which had started thirty years earlier in her Robinson Crusoe–style homemade lab.

More and more experiments were conducted and researchers never stopped advancing in the field. By the early 1970s, NGF was recognized as an important subject of research in neuroscience. Rita was invited to write a chapter on this specific topic in a textbook entitled *The Neurosciences: Paths of Discovery*.[122] She confidently reiterated in other publications that "it stands out today as one of the best known hormonal and growth factors, and its long-sought mechanism and site of action are slowly but steadily coming into focus."[123]

In the late seventies, Rita's two research teams, as well as others, started discovering that nerve growth factor affected more than just nerves. First, they discovered a link between NGF and the adrenal glands, part of the endocrine system. Then they linked NGF to the immune system, which defends the body against attacks by bacteria and viruses. This discovery was sensational: Very few scientists had even considered the possibility of demonstrating a connection between the nervous system and the immune system.[124]

Rita found it difficult to accept, however, that researchers outside her own two groups could conduct experiments on what she considered her own creature. The identification of the "wonder molecule" represented for Rita a generative act, comparable to giving birth to a child.[125] It was a challenge to acknowledge that by then NGF was studied outside of Italy, not only within the Washington University team, but also by a Swiss group led by Hans Thoenen at the University of Basel and another headed by Silvio Varon at the University of California, San Diego. Given the unethical behavior of some of her colleagues, Rita became rather possessive and territorial, and not unreasonably so. She viewed NGF as her specific field of action, and sometimes had to bravely defend herself and her findings, as she did at the Massachusetts Institute of Technology (MIT) in Cambridge. In spite of her English—still spoken with a strong Italian accent after so many years in the United States—she talked to a large audience, particularly trained in dialectical discourse, and brilliantly responded to their insidious questions.

Rita was extremely generous and patient and would move mountains to help people in need. However, she could be cutting and intolerant when she clearly perceived that unethical young people were disrespectful of the work of their predecessors, so that they could claim full merit for subsequent discoveries themselves. She had never experienced professional discrimination in the US, but she thought that her work was being ignored because of her age. For the first time she felt vulnerable vis-à-vis the aggressiveness of young, ambitious, unscrupulous researchers who were determined to reach professional success by all means.

In an interview on Italian television, she disclosed that already a year before she was awarded the Nobel Prize, the same people who had contested her merits organized a conference in her honor in California and those she thought the most hostile turned out to be the most friendly.

Rita's best ally had been her intrinsic optimism and the conviction that in the end, truth would always win out. She may have exaggerated when in the seventies she declared that she had been rejected or forgotten, because in those years she was elected to the US National Academy of Sciences—an honor given only to nine other women before her. She was also the first woman to be invited by Pope Paul VI to become a member of the Pontifical Academy of Sciences, with which Galileo had once been associated. Moreover, Rita soon after received her first honorary degree at Uppsala University, Sweden, quite an unexpected achievement.

When she found out that one of her favorite colleagues, Renato Dulbecco, thanks to his study of tumor viruses, had won the Nobel Prize in Physiology or Medicine in 1975, Rita was truly elated. It was indeed a rare happening, perhaps the first time in the history of the Nobel Prize, that a professor, along with two of his students, David Baltimore and Howard Temin, shared the greatest achievement in the field. Renato was sixty-one, and his scientific recognition in Stockholm represented a great honor for Italy and in particular for the University of Turin.

Rita was exceedingly proud of being a "talent scout," having met Renato at the University of Turin. She was instrumental in charting the professional future of her younger friend, first by urging him to transfer from pathological anatomy to physics, then by convincing Professor Levi to offer him a position as assistant. She also wrote to her family friend and colleague Salvador Luria, by then a full professor in the US, suggesting that he invite Renato to work with him for a year at the University of Indiana. The fellowship he accepted radically changed his life. When he embarked with Rita for the US, he had decided that his future was in the new continent. Once in the States, they became close friends. Rita, Renato, and Salvador had much in common: They had graduated in medicine in Turin, yet they chose not to work as doctors but dedicate their lives to research. Each time they reached an objective, they would meet to celebrate and devise a common way to further scientific progress. They did this throughout their lives in the States.

Renato was the first person Rita informed about her revolutionary hypothesis in January 1951, which led to the identification of the humoral character of what she had called in her letters home "the nerve growth promoting agent." Needless to say, Rita was very uplifted by his unconditional scientific endorsement.[126]

After the Nobel, Dulbecco continued to study the genetics of cancer until his retirement. Rita's professional life was deeply intertwined with Renato's. The two scientists kept participating as speakers in the same congresses all over the world. They kept sharing their aspirations and dreams, and their friendship proved to be a gift to be treasured for life.

Chapter Ten

A NEW LIFE IN ITALY

In 1977, Rita retired as professor emeritus of biology from Washington University, where she had performed most of her research since 1947. She finally bid goodbye for good to the country where she was supposed to stay just for one semester, thirty years before.

In 1979, at the age of seventy, Rita formally resigned as director of the Laboratory of Cell Biology in Rome as well, but she was allowed to continue to work as a guest professor at the institute for another ten years.

Rita had no intention of retiring after she moved back to Italy. "If you stop working, you are dead," she used to say—an existential belief that she shared with Renato Dulbecco. She kept on researching, traveling, and, most of all, fighting for meaningful causes.

The time had come for her to seek ways to draw on all she had learned, and to give back to others, by engaging with social issues. In 1983, among other awards, she accepted the Louisa Gross Horwitz Prize, along with Stanley Cohen and Viktor Hamburger. This prize is awarded annually by Columbia University in New York to a researcher or group of researchers who make an outstanding contribution in the fields of biology or biochemistry.

At the same time, she agreed to become the president of the Italian Multiple Sclerosis Society (AISM) and served for many years, supporting the prevention and the identification of an effective therapy.

In 1985 the validity of Rita's latest research at the Laboratory of Cell Biology was fully recognized by Luigi Rossi Bernardi, who had the power to found an Institute of Neurobiology and entrust its directorship to Pietro Calissano, so that there would be a continuity of approach and vision. It was a particularly satisfactory recognition a few months before the conferral of the Nobel Prize.

In 1986 Rita had gone to New York to receive, along with Stanley Cohen, the most prestigious scientific award in the United States: the Albert Lasker award at Rockefeller University for basic medical research. This prize is often a prelude to a Nobel in Medicine, as indeed it proved on this occasion.

Just ten days later, at about eleven o'clock in the morning on October 13, the telephone rang in her elegant apartment on Via di Villa Massimo in Rome. A call from Stockholm announced to Rita that she had been awarded the Nobel Prize in Physiology or Medicine. She was only the fourth woman to win this category of prize, and she was the first Italian woman to be honored with a Nobel in any area of science. She would share it with Stanley Cohen, the biochemist she had worked with in St. Louis during the most intense years of her career. Rita was then seventy-seven years old, and Stan, sixty-four.

In her autobiography, Rita does not clearly specify that she was awarded the Nobel Prize. Instead, she hints at the event as if it took place in a fable. In a way, she downplays her discovery by anthropomorphizing the nerve growth factor itself, turning it into the same elusive masked reveler she met in Rio, now "wrapped in a black cape" for this royal occasion. Bowing to the king but looking straight at Rita, he lowers his mask, revealing his identity for a fleeting instant, which fulfills her desire as they recognize each other. As in a fairy tale, he appears and disappears; his mission and hers have at last been accomplished.

On this magical night in Stockholm where she would receive the Nobel, Rita's regal velvet dress in deep green, red amaranth, and purple was certainly worthy of her Prince Charming. She eventually gave her "Cinderella" dress back to its designer, Roberto Capucci, to be displayed, along with his whole museum collection, at Villa Manin, an eighteenth-century villa in Passariano, near Udine. Rita was the only scientist Capucci ever dressed. In the panoply of great ladies who attended his atelier, she enjoyed the highest consideration, along with actress Silvana Mangano, whom he majestically transformed in Pier Paolo Pasolini's film *Teorema*.

Rita donated her share of the Nobel Prize sum to various charities and to the restoration of Jewish monuments in Italy, a gesture in keeping with her constant generosity.

Pietro Calissano concisely identified what he called the three steps that led Rita toward Stockholm to receive the Nobel Prize. The first one occurred in 1951, like an epiphany, in the lab in St. Louis, after she read a brief article about an experiment that one of Viktor Hamburger's students, Elmer Bueker, had published.

In her book *Cronologia di una scoperta* (*Chronology of a Discovery*), Rita admitted that her intuition became a certitude long before she obtained the supporting evidence in its favor.[127] Only in Rio de Janeiro—in Hertha Meyer's tissue culture laboratory at the Institute of Biophysics, while repeating in vitro the same experiments she had done in vivo at Washington University—did she finally obtain conclusive evidence that the X growth factor was a liquid, and this was the second step toward the Nobel Prize. This substance, however, would be identified from a chemical point of view, upon her return from Brazil, by biochemist Stanley Cohen, who became her associate. The two scientific explorers, after deciding to call the mysterious factor "nerve growth factor," or NGF, and daringly experimenting with the venom of a poisonous snake in place of a mouse tumor, gradually came to the conclusion that it was indeed a molecule. And this was a major turning point, the third and final step.

In the presentation speech by Kerstin Hall of the 1986 Nobel Prize awarded to Rita Levi-Montalcini and Stanley Cohen for the pioneering identification of nerve growth factor (NGF) and epidermal growth factor (EGF), it was highlighted that:

- The discovery, identification, and isolation of NGF

created a breakthrough in the research field of developmental neurobiology and held great promise in the treatment of central nervous system diseases.

- Cohen's EGF had been found to help heal wounds in the eye's cornea, the skin, and the intestines, as well as being efficacious in the treatment of burns.[128]

When Rita was asked to comment on the meaning of her finding, she stated: "With NGF I just discovered the tip of an iceberg which I have then further explored. However, there are many secrets that *we* have yet to discover." She modestly used the *pluralis majestatis* because she was fully aware and convinced that scientific accomplishment is the result of teamwork.

As soon as the news of the Nobel reached the media, Salvador Luria's comment to the press was that the prize should have been awarded to Rita much earlier. He underlined how her finding had opened a complex and articulate new page in neurosciences. Her "wonder molecule" was having a great impact, though indirectly, on the study of cancer, on degenerative illnesses such as Alzheimer's, and even on ocular neurodegenerative diseases.

Some researchers, however, thought that Viktor Hamburger should have been included in the prize, given his strong support and involvement since the 1930s, which paved the way to Rita's and Stan's future findings. In an interview in 1988, Rita was perhaps misunderstood when she pointed out that Professor Hamburger had not been in Brazil, where she had discovered clear validation of her finding. Though they had published two papers together, Hamburger humbly admitted that "all the observations and the experiments were done by her" and that he was just the chairman of the department. He was very busy and not directly involved in the actual laboratory work. They were, however, in constant communication. She would regularly show him the slides of her new findings and he always encouraged her because she was "an extremely ingenious woman." Rita had been very territorial in establishing her maternal credentials of NGF, specifying early on in her correspondence with her family that though she had kept Hamburger constantly informed, it was she, and only she, who did all the work in the lab.

According to Pietro Calissano, Rita's statement, which was inaccurately reported by the press, caused a deterioration of Viktor and Rita's long relationship of trust and friendship to the point that when she visited St. Louis in October 1991, the ninety-one-year-old Hamburger did not make the time to have dinner with her.[129] She often tried to contact him and explain, but in the meantime Professor Hamburger died, leaving Rita with a deep scar of regret.

In early September 1995, furthermore, *Dagens Nyheter*, apparently one of the most influential Swedish newspapers, published an article that caused a real stir by claiming that Fidia, an Italian pharmaceutical company, had pressured the Nobel committee to give the 1986 prize to Rita.[130] The Nobel committee, through its director Michael Sohlman, and the whole scientific community vehemently rejected these charges and *Dagens Nyheter* was forced to retract the accusation. It was proven that awarding the Nobel to Rita had been proposed at least four times since 1965 by hundreds of scientists, but the overall majority was not reached until 1986.

The painful and intricate debate came to an end with a clear statement by *Dagens Nyheter* that Rita Levi-Montalcini's worthiness had never been questioned. Rita refused to comment, maintaining that by slandering the Nobel Prize, the media would denigrate not her, but the whole national and international scientific community. She was convinced, however, that "if we forbid industry to help the lab research, we die." For Rita, scientific research was a mission to be practiced without any political or religious preconceptions and it ultimately worked for the cultural growth of the whole nation.[131]

Chapter Eleven

THE NOBEL PRIZE AND ITS IMPACT

As Rita pointed out in an interview on Italian TV, after the Nobel Prize she received thousands of letters, as well as so many applications and requests that she found it difficult to work. Only several months later was she able to get back to her usual routine: a wakeup call between 4:00 and 5:00 a.m. in order to study until 9:00 a.m.; then from 9:00 a.m. to 1:00 p.m., experiments in the lab with her assistants.

After she received the National Medal of Science from the hands of President Ronald Reagan at the White House in 1987, she was granted over twenty honorary degrees worldwide, from Bologna to Cambridge, Massachusetts (Harvard University), to London to Buenos Aires. She was also the recipient of innumerable scientific prizes and honorary citizenships from the most diverse cities of Italy, such as Reggio Calabria, Sassari, and Turin, her hometown.

During this period, Rita's interest in literature was rekindled and her childhood ambition to become a writer was finally fulfilled. Besides making the time to read her favorite authors and poets, from Primo Levi to William Butler Yeats, she decided first of all to dedicate herself to writing her autobiography. In 1987 *Elogio dell'imperfezione* was published, and later translated into English with the title of *In Praise of Imperfection: My Life and Work* (1988), in which she did not limit herself to recounting her unique story as a shy and insecure Jewish-Italian girl becoming an internationally known scientist. She also described the virtues of the American working environment and the limits of the Italian scientific system, not for the mere sake of criticism, but in order to encourage a positive change in the Italian approach to research.

Rita was by her very nature invigorated by challenges and had no intention of surrendering to the obstacles created by intricate Italian governmental policies; going back to her own country had been the dream of her postwar life. Salvador Luria, the first and the youngest of the three friends to be awarded a Nobel in Medicine, died in New England in 1991 and fought his scientific and ethical battles in the New World, never wishing to conclude his career in Italy. Renato Dulbecco, inspired by Rita, had, on the request of the Italian National Research Council (CNR), tried to start an ambitious project of biotechnological research (the Italian human genome) by establishing a lab in Milan, with the ultimate goal of deciphering the differences in the cancer genome. Rita was very pleased to have found in her friend an ally in making Italian research acquire international relevance. After six years, however, Renato returned to the Salk

Institute in California, as president emeritus, disillusioned by Italian bureaucracy and the endemic lack of funding.

In July 1992, Rita—still a public figure at the age of eighty-three, appreciated and much sought after—decided not only to persist, but also to found, along with her twin sister, the Levi-Montalcini Onlus Foundation, dedicated to the memory of their father, Adamo Levi, with the motto "The future belongs to the young." Their objective was to fight illiteracy at all levels.

Increasingly, Rita's social engagement became a deeply felt inner necessity. She recognized how lucky she had been compared with most of womankind, and she had great plans for other women, because she was convinced that they were as intelligent as men, though different. To be different, however, did not mean to be inferior. She decided it was time to act by investing money and energy to promote literacy and education, especially of African women, through a number of scholarships and fellowships. Her goal was to show solidarity and to give them a way to gain self-esteem and dignity after suffering psychological and physical abuse ranging from rape to incest and infibulation. In this way, social and working marginalization, cultural violence, and barbaric, male-authored traditions would be, if not finally uprooted, at least reduced. All of her adult life, Rita had been interested in the emancipation of women, seeing a strong link between the discrimination she had suffered as a Jew in Italy during the Second World War and the way women in Africa were treated. Through her foundation, she was able to help more than ten thousand African women reach their goals of attending medical school or increasing self-awareness and developing know-how in different fields, including trade. She also promoted the creation of over one hundred micro companies or self-supporting co-ops.[132] She did all of this because she believed that helping a woman would mean helping a family, if not a whole nation.

Counting on the support of the European Union and UNESCO, Rita was also instrumental in creating WIN (Women's International Network for Emergency and Solidarity), founded in 1995 in Rome with sociologist Eleonora Barbieri Masini, to help women in threatening situations, from debt to drugs, from disease to forced prostitution.

She was convinced that in every country, social and economic disparity had always privileged members of the male gender, excluding women for a long time from positions of responsibility at every level. On many occasions and with great conviction and passion, she would point out that only less than 10% of positions in the political, social, scientific, and economic fields were occupied by females, while "human society is made of men and women and it should be represented by both." According to Rita women were multitaskers by nature, being gifted with adaptability and flexibility. She firmly believed that the art of war had been invented and managed exclusively by men.[133] Rita was obviously thinking of her own youth during a period of fear, hatred, and violence under the despotic rule of Mussolini and Hitler. She was also referring to Auschwitz, Treblinka, Mauthausen, and all the other concentration camps as having been exclusively male creations.

While she was hoping for a better and more peaceful life on

this planet, she watched such developments as the Cold War, missile crises, nuclear standoffs, earth-threatening pollution, wars, terrorist attacks, and genocidal massacres in the Far East, the Middle East, Africa, Europe, and the Americas.[134] Moreover, men still seemed to favor an economy of weapons and therefore of death, with ever-growing militarization, jeopardizing peace, which is after all the only condition to guarantee the survival of the human species.

Given these premises, Rita maintained that a radical change was needed, not circumscribed to marginalized, underdeveloped areas, but central to a global society needing to cope with technological, economic, and political changes in the third millennium.

Universal suffrage in the US (1920) and in Italy (1948) had marked two major steps in a positive direction, but there was so much work still to be done. Rita suggested that women's qualities should be capitalized upon because they are essential to progress toward peace, tolerance, and equality. On this topic she had a lot to say and fight for, and did so in front of large audiences of fans. The problem was not only to give women a sense of dignity as thinking beings, intellectually and morally responsible for their actions, but also to finally liberate them from their social confinement to the private sphere, freeing potential that had lain untapped for millennia.[135] In fact, when Rita became an American citizen, she added her mother's maiden name, Montalcini, to Levi, her father's family name. Upon returning to Italy she regained her Italian citizenship while keeping the extended family name. This was her own way to pay tribute to her mother, who upon her marriage had relinquished the opportunity to develop her talents as an artist.

Rita was a feminist sui generis. She believed in women rather than in feminist movements. In her book entitled *Eva era africana* (*Eve Was African*), Rita wrote extensively on the 1974 discovery in the Afar desert, Ethiopia, of the skeleton of the first human being, a woman, named "Lucy" by paleoanthropologists Donald Johanson and Tom Gray.[136] Everything started three million years ago and Africa is now widely recognized as the cradle of modern humankind. Rita recounted the stories of many local women, such as Nahid Toubia, a gynecologist who fought for years against genital mutilation, and Wangari Maathai, the first African woman to win the Nobel Prize for Peace. They had transformed themselves from voiceless witnesses into major protagonists of the socio-cultural rebirth of Africa. Education and culture proved to be the only efficient means to build a better future for themselves and their children.

Rita's enlightened dream was to see all women of the poorest and most neglected areas on the planet fight for emancipation from marginalization through traditional and digital forms of education, thanks to the internet.[137]

Rita continued to be such an outspoken magnetic personality in the Italian cultural and scientific panorama that she was asked by the president of the Italian Republic, Oscar Luigi Scalfaro, to be the first scientist to preside over the *Istituto della Enciclopedia Italiana* founded by Giovanni Treccani, which she did from 1993 to 1998. She first declined the offer out of modesty, but when it was persistently pointed out to her that the institution needed to renew itself by choosing a personality outside the traditional humanistic milieu, she agreed to accept one more challenge. Rita had the invaluable quality of being a flexible leader, able to rethink and revise her points of view.

She included right away a staff of internationally acclaimed scientists, as well as a few colleagues who had been awarded the Nobel Prize in Physiology or Medicine, such as Renato Dulbecco and David Baltimore. As usual, she followed her trusty ethical compass by privileging professional merit over nationality or friendship.

Rita agreed to edit a work in four volumes, *Frontiere della vita* (*Frontiers of Life*), which was translated into English because of the high level of the scholars involved. It turned into an international scientific and commercial success and was declared the best educational project of the year. This specific project provided an innovative opportunity to export into the Anglo-Saxon world a scientific work, entirely conceived and realized in Italy, against the general trend, which was to translate biomedical publications from English into Italian.[138]

At the same time, Rita was also able to write ten books in Italian. Some have been translated into French, some into German. Only one, her autobiography, is available to English-language readers. Once she identified her topic, she would systematically buy a number of texts, mark them with yellow Post-It notes, and highlight key concepts and information. She would start writing, elaborating on the text, and devoting great attention to choosing the most appropriate title for each chapter. Even after winning the Nobel Prize, she kept on using an old typewriter, but she gradually came to prefer more modern technologies.

Her autobiography, *In Praise of Imperfection*, stressed the fact that the human brain is imperfect and therefore able to evolve and change compared to the brain of any insect, which is, on its terms, perfect and complete. Rita humbly and joyfully accepted the human condition in all its complexity and contradictions and encouraged young people to hold onto their dreams and aspirations. In *Il tuo futuro* (*Your Future*), one of her first books, she urges adolescents and young adults not to be spectators but actors on the world stage of the third millennium, and to accept the difficult task of choosing the right path to build their own future.[139]

In *La galassia mente* (*The Galaxy of the Mind*),[140] she explores the origins of the mind both from a scientific point of view, dealing with cells and neurons, as well as from a more elusive emotional perspective. She also retraces step by step the evolution of the nervous system to better explain the formidable structure of the human brain and present a system of ethical values for future generations.

Cantico di una vita is a selection of about 200 letters from the more than 1,500 that she wrote to her mother and twin sister about her experience in the US from 1947 to 1977. Here her true passions emerge: the strong bond with her whole family in Turin; the relentless, stoic commitment to her scientific vocation expressed by her everyday routine in the lab; the need to constantly help others.

A triptych followed—*Tempo di mutamenti*,[141] *Tempo di*

azione,[142] and *Tempo di revisione*[143] (*Time for Changes, Time for Action,* and *Time for Review*)—sharing the idea that from childhood on, individuals should be educated according to cognitive methods, instead of authoritarian or permissive systems. The child should not be a passive receiver of knowledge but an active participant. According to Rita, young people should be assisted and advised to become curious about what surrounds them. In each of these three books she underlines how society is still fundamentally patriarchal and has created a disparity between males and females. She invites younger generations to stand up for their own rights, keeping in mind that rights do not exclude duties, in view of reaching acceptable living conditions for the generations to come.

These three books are thematically similar to the *Declaration of Human Duties* she wrote in 1992, and later submitted to the United Nations. It is a sort of *Magna Carta* stressing the importance of human values as the underlying key to world change as well as a new moral contract between old and new generations.

Rita's strong ethical and scientific convictions are reiterated in other publications such as *Abbi il coraggio di conoscere*[144] and *Rita Levi-Montalcini racconta la scuola ai ragazzi* (*Rita Levi-Montalcini Tells Children About School*).[145] She underlines once again that education is the basis of a free society and that children and young adults should be taught not only the cultural heritage of their predecessors, but also the fundamental values that make life worth living.

I nuovi magellani nell'er@ digitale (*The New Magellans in the*

Digital Age)[146] is also dedicated to young people, seen as new Magellans or contemporary voyagers on the way to knowledge in the digital era. Nowadays, in many countries of the globe, critical issues such as poverty, racism, illiteracy, and denial of civic rights have to be faced. The new Magellans can circumnavigate the earth without moving from home, and dialogue in real time with any inhabitant of the planet. It is the responsibility of these young virtual explorers to identify the problems of the planet and find solutions that allow the survival and the proper development of the entire human species.

L'altra parte del mondo (*The Other Part of the World*)[147] analyzes the global objectives of the third millennium: eradication of poverty, which represents a major problem for over half of the world; elimination of illiteracy through universal education; defeat of inequality between men and women; and protection of the environment in order to safeguard the health and well-being of families. Rita believed that only a global partnership among governments and international institutions could achieve the best results in this direction.

Cronologia di una scoperta (*Chronology of a Discovery*),[148] published on the occasion of her one-hundredth birthday, explores step by step the challenging saga of her groundbreaking discovery of NGF, which led her to the Nobel Prize.

An even higher form of recognition than the coveted Swedish award arrived in August 2001, when Rita received an unexpected telephone call from Carlo Azeglio Ciampi, president of the Italian Republic, announcing her appointment as life senator. She was still mourning the deaths from the previous year of her sister Nina and of her beloved twin, Paola. Her elder sister, who had been so influential in Rita's childhood, died in Turin, where she had lived most of her life after her marriage with a distant relative, Ulrico Montalcini, a diamond merchant. This loss was particularly harsh for Rita because she was left with the deep regret that Nina had sacrificed all her life to family duties rather than fulfill her humanistic and intellectual talents, as she herself had done in science. A few months later her grief became almost unbearable when Paola succumbed to her long illness. Rita thought the world had come to an end—the house was so empty without Paola's comforting and inspiring presence. Ciampi's telephone call, however, brought a new light into her twinkling greenish eyes. She was so surprised and grateful that she was almost speechless. The president had to repeat twice his decision to appoint her "life senator for scientific and social merits."

Rita felt the utmost gratification, even more than the Nobel Prize, because it came from her own country. In a way it justified her thirty-year emigration to the United States, fulfilling her aspiration to come back to Italy and take up a prestigious role in the world of science. She was the second woman in the history of the Italian Republic to obtain this title. The peak of Rita's civic engagement had been achieved. Rita was appointed life senator along with Mario Luzi (literature), Sergio Pininfarina (industry), and Giorgio Napolitano and Emilio Colombo, former leading politicians (social merits). She was ninety-two when, on September 25, 2001, she officially entered Palazzo Madama, welcomed by a standing ovation. From that day on, she conscientiously performed her senatorial duties. She loved her country so much that when she was asked, along with the other life senators, to vote to maintain the fragile government majority of Romano Prodi during the 2006–2008 parliamentary term, she spent the necessary long hours at the Senate in spite of her age.

Rita knew very well that, as a life senator, she was even more of a role model. Writer Dacia Maraini called Rita's recognition "a success for all Italian women." Only in 1976 had Tina Anselmi become minister of labor, the first woman cabinet member in Italy. With too few exceptions, Italian political life had been, and continues to be, almost exclusively a male territory.

Motivated by a strong sense of civic and moral duty, Rita went to the Senate every day. She enhanced the prestige of the highest Italian political institution with her wisdom and scientific know-how. She became familiar with other colleagues, in particular with Gianni Agnelli, also from Turin. Both of them were known internationally, had mingled with kings and queens, had been received by heads of state, and welcomed, among other places, at the White House. Until Rita was 103, she spent long hours impassively, even stoically, exercising her right to vote, in full possession of her mental and physical faculties—as indeed required by Article 59 of the Italian Constitution. She maintained that she did this because the worst evil of our time is indifference toward the fundamental values in life.

Rita also dedicated the last decade of her existence to establishing a specifically European brain research center. She launched the idea of this unique facility at the yearly forum for top leaders in the Italian business and industrial community at Cernobbio, near Lake Como. But the question was: Where should it be located? To her surprise, four cities in Italy quickly volunteered to host it: Trieste, Varese, Turin, and Rome. A committee of scientists, including Renato Dulbecco, evaluated each offer.

The final choice was Rome, where the Santa Lucia Scientific Institute for Research, Hospitalization, and Healthcare could provide a space of more than six acres (25,000 square meters), which, once restored, would host the new group of researchers, alongside those of Santa Lucia itself and of the Italian National Research Council's Neurological Institute. The agreement envisaged that the Santa Lucia Institute would be responsible for the restoration expenses.[149]

The new center would be named the European Brain Research Institute (EBRI). Its mission was and still is "the study of the central nervous system, from the neurons to the whole brain, in health and diseases." It would focus on research aimed at understanding neurological and especially degenerative diseases, such as Alzheimer's, Parkinson's, Huntington's, and ALS, also known as Lou Gehrig's disease, an illness that produces progressively worsening neuromuscular weakness.[150] Realizing it was possible to use her own name and fame to promote this cause, Rita fought to make EBRI one of the world's leading centers in the field. Her life aspiration to leave a permanent mark on the international scientific scene would be ultimately fulfilled.

The official opening was on April 20, 2005, attended by a large number of political personalities at provincial, regional, and national levels—an institutional miracle. It started as a consortium of four major institutions, including about 150 researchers and counting on adequate technical and administrative support. Everybody praised the key role of scientific research in modern society and concurred with the necessity of nurturing young people in Italy to do this work.

However, unlike CNR and other institutions, EBRI was private and could not count on government funding to pay salaries and the costs of maintenance of the whole establishment. The idyll between private and public in this ambitious project did not last long. After four years, in spite of Rita's scientific charisma and reputation, the center was on the brink of closing. Many nerve-racking vicissitudes, due mainly to political inertia and, once again, lack of funding, led Rita, as always unwavering in her passion and commitment, to finally untie EBRI from the initial consortium. It was transferred to an independent building of 12,900 square feet (1,200 square meters) at the Sapienza University of Rome, and continues its activity to this day. The present staff now consists of more than sixty researchers, including PhD students and fellowship recipients. The funding comes from single scientific projects, the Italian Ministry of Education and Research, and national and international pharmaceutical industries. Research is blossoming because Rita's molecule of life, NGF, opened an extremely broad field of study, including cardiovascular diseases and ocular pathologies.

In her nineties, Rita had to cope with macular degeneration, a disease affecting the retina. She underwent an operation in Switzerland, but gradually her sight worsened. When her close collaborator Luigi Aloe had discovered that NGF also acted on the ocular system, Rita had it purified and decided to experiment with the molecule she had discovered. She bravely used it for years on herself and managed to stabilize the damaged part of the retina, without any side effects. She responded to this extraordinary further finding by Luigi with a postcard portraying a composer playing the piano and saying, "I have the feeling we will have to listen to Bach again."

Rita was a lifetime pioneer in neuroscience; until the end, she interacted every day with her students, stressing that the brain had to be researched both in a state of health and of illness, and giving them guidelines for their future. To become a scientific researcher, she maintained, enthusiasm and competence are needed, as well as intuition, creativity, and total dedication.

She came to represent a mode of life entirely committed to research and scientific innovation. She wanted specific work on the human brain to continue after her death in the strong conviction that though our bodies are meant to die, our values and humanistic ideals are not. Rita's selfless work for the good of humanity and for the expansion of scientific knowledge came to ultimate fruition in EBRI.

No doubt this institution will strive to keep alive her vision as well as her name and her lifelong engagement with the study of the brain, the most intricate and fascinating organ of the human body.

Chapter Twelve

AN ENLIGHTENED ATTITUDE TO AGING

The brain is like a parachute. If you do not keep it open, it serves no purpose.

—LORD THOMAS ROBERT DEWAR

Rita became an active centenarian without ever feeling her chronological age.

Her one-hundredth birthday in 2009 was celebrated in Rome with a special event at the Quirinale, the Italian presidential residence, with President Giorgio Napolitano in attendance, along with an exclusive circle of senators and Nobel Prize winners. Another great event in her honor was hosted by the mayor and held in the Palazzo del Campidoglio, where a great number of guests—the Roman intelligentsia as well as friends, acquaintances, and fans—gathered to celebrate the world-renowned scientist.

Her sight and hearing were greatly impaired, yet she was

very alert, elegant, and thoroughly up to the occasion. She stood straight, impeccably dressed and coiffed, ready to cut the first slice of the enormous cake, decorated with fresh strawberries, prepared in her honor. Thanks to the relentless self-discipline practiced every day of her life, she was able to withstand the demands of this special occasion with grace and elegance. Thousands of people all around her yearned to discover the secret of her success and to witness at least a tiny fragment of her greatness. Whenever asked to comment on her achievements, she would bluntly state that they were the result of study, work, and the fostering of trust in her own abilities. She was a slight woman, gossamer thin in appearance, but her presence was extraordinarily imposing.[151] When Rita was about to cut the cake, an attendant next to her tried timidly to help her steady the knife in her hand, but she managed to rise to the requirements of the ritual with complete autonomy and was warmly applauded.

There followed other celebrations of her birthday at the Senate House, as well as in a number of universities, theaters, and private homes in many cities, including her beloved Turin. While she did not much like to shake hands with everybody, she did not mind being photographed. It took her many decades to overcome the shyness of her adolescence and she did so by cultivating her self-confidence and by conquering her self-consciousness about her appearance. She had been convinced since childhood that she was rather plain and only moderately intelligent, and that therefore she needed to exert tenacity, determination, perseverance, and optimism to reach her objectives. She gradually learned to pay attention to her hair as well as to her clothes and jewelry, which she carefully designed herself. She always wanted to wear something unique, something that would show her personality. "Every achievement in my life," she often stated, "has been the result of willpower and effort, and not chance or luck." Nobody in her family, no Italian woman life senator, and no Nobel Prize winner had reached the age of one hundred before her. And this on its own was quite an achievement.

Rita was a dreamer and a revolutionary, and yet a down-to-earth hard worker. She had a larger-than-life personality and a particularly generous nature. Once she had achieved international recognition, she wanted to share her accomplishments and contribute to the well-being of those less fortunate than herself.

It was after she was awarded the Nobel Prize that she had the time to further explore the regenerative power of the brain and its potential for creativity, even in aging subjects such as herself. The result of her research was the elaboration of original and radical theories on old age. In *Abbi il coraggio di conoscere*, a book she wrote when she turned ninety-five, in the chapter significantly titled "*Il cervello non deve mai andare in pensione*" ("The brain should never retire"), she cogently states her views on the topic of the aging brain. To set the tone of the book, she quotes a poem by Maria Luisa Spaziani, a renowned poet from her native Turin, inviting the reader to acknowledge the limitless possibilities of the human brain and to rely on its creative power:

*Thought has no Pillars of Hercules
It is your small soul,*

So diabolically lazy that creates them.
Neither Ulysses nor Columbus had an inkling
Of the thousands of islands waiting out there.

Whole continents await you.
They are dormant in your brain: dare!
There's a world to be created.

In her book, Rita also quotes Immanuel Kant's motto *sapere aude* ("dare to know") and states her conviction that the philosopher's challenge is in our time more relevant than ever. In her view, in fact, the greatest privilege accorded to human beings is the capacity to use their mental faculties in every stage of life, particularly in old age. She firmly believed that our cognitive faculties, namely those involved in the acquisition of knowledge, are our greatest asset.

In her later years Rita stated that her interest in the body lessened in comparison to her curiosity about the mind, even though she very much wanted to delay her physical decline. She was nicknamed *"l'eterna ventenne"* ("the eternal twenty-year-old") by her friends and acquaintances because she continued to keep up the level of energy required to sustain the demands of her work, to which she remained devoted until the last days of her long life. It was important to her to be an exemplary woman in command of both her mental faculties and her physical appearance.

With conviction and audacity, Rita set out to challenge popular misconceptions regarding the aging brain and to debunk the demeaning common myths associated with old age. She provided scientific evidence that regardless of the fact that from the age of sixty onward, hundreds of thousands of neurons face a programmed death every day, it is equally true that an astronomic number of other cells simultaneously compensate for those deaths with alternative developmental processes. Although, according to recent neurological studies, every ten years we lose 10 percent of our neurons, their decrease is not uniform and the cells that remain alive can increase in number, branch out, and trigger the development of cerebral circuits. These regenerative-compensatory processes of the brain accord individuals the opportunity for long-lasting intellectual activity. In fact, the more we exercise our intellectual faculties, the more we foster the regenerative-compensatory cerebral processes. Rita anticipated the new science of neuroplasticity, maintaining— also out of her own personal experience—that the brain, far from being fixed, has remarkable powers of changing its own structure and compensating for even the most challenging neurological conditions. She foresaw new frontiers of brain science.

For Rita, the adjective "old" in the expression "old age," with respect to the brain, takes on meanings very different from those commonly or conventionally attributed to it. She wrote a whole book on this topic, *L'asso nella manica a brandelli* (*The Ace Up the Tattered Sleeve*). Its incipit is once again a poem, this time by her favorite Irish poet, William Butler Yeats:

An aged man is but a paltry thing.

A tattered coat upon a stick, unless
Soul clap its hands and sing, and louder sing
For every tatter in its mortal dress.[152]

Yeats draws a poignant representation of the aged human being in whom the paltriness of the body, due to inevitable decline, is more than compensated for and ultimately altogether redeemed by the vigorous and joyful vitality of the mind. This powerful image perfectly reflects Rita's convictions regarding the indomitable power of the brain and her philosophy of aging.

Old age should not be lived lingering in the memory of the past, but in "planning one's activity for the time that is left, whether a day, a month, or years to come," in the hope of carrying out projects that in our youth it was not possible to realize. She totally agreed with Marcus Tullius Cicero, the Roman statesman and philosopher, who, in *Cato Maior de Senectute*, referred to the life of Cato the Elder as an example to follow:

Life follows a very precise path and it enriches every stage with its own qualities. It is for this reason that the vulnerability of children, the impetuousness of young people, the gravity of adults, and the maturity of old age are entirely natural characteristics and should be appreciated each at the proper time. In truth, when old age is allowed to accomplish the same tasks as in youth, it certainly succeeds in doing so even better. It is not strength, physical ability, or swiftness that bring about great achievements but rather wisdom, foresight, and judgment. These are qualities that old age is not deprived of, but on the contrary it can widely take advantage of.[153]

Rita was incredibly surprised by Cicero's radical approach because in Roman times or even later, it was not common knowledge that the physical decline of the human body does not necessarily run parallel with that of the brain, the complex organ where the mental activities of *homo sapiens* take place.

So many great men from Michelangelo Buonarroti and Galileo Galilei to Bertrand Russell and Pablo Picasso confirmed this theory and affirmed, with their creative works, that formidable cognitive faculties persist also in new ways later on in life, in the so-called "third age." This is a phenomenon that may appear paradoxical; instead, it is proven by incontestable scientific data. Michelangelo died at age eighty-nine in 1564; Galileo at seventy-eight in 1642; Picasso at ninety-two in 1973. They all produced, approaching their eighties or nineties, masterpieces recognized by the whole world.

Third-age learning usually takes place in the retirement years for those who keep their brains and bodies active and meet stimulating new friends. In democratic countries with a high industrial and cultural degree of development, this is a distinct possibility for privileged people. Rita underlined, however, that nine out of ten of individuals cannot, because they live under dictatorial regimes or are afflicted by endemic illnesses, hunger, or social impositions based on political or religious creeds that prevent people of the so-called developing nations from expressing their full intellectual potential.[154]

Rita acknowledged, however, that third-age learning was not an automatic solution to the threat of mental deterioration. She stressed that humans in old age can present a dramatic senile decline basically due to three factors: a longer life, the wear and tear of the organs, and the possible marginalization of the elderly person by society.

She was often asked in her eighties and nineties if she still studied. Her prompt answer was always the same: "Certainly, more than when I was young. I work every day in the lab with many young researchers. I am happy, and they are too." She believed that the brain, even in advanced age, retained great plasticity as well as intellectual potential.

Rita's positive theory about aging is in contrast with the pessimistic views of French intellectual Simone de Beauvoir. In her voluminous treatise about the third age, de Beauvoir declared that the majority of humankind adapts itself to old age with sadness or with rebellion, because it inspires loathing more than death itself.[155]

The secret for Rita was to age well, meaning that the brain should never "retire," but instead keep using its intellectual faculties at the highest level. While the other organs wear out, the brain does not. Paradoxically, the more it is used, the sharper it becomes. Moreover, Rita objected to de Beauvoir's statement that the old person is always rejected by the community, underlining how, in many patriarchal societies at different times, old people have been accepted as a respected and integral part of society.

Unfortunately, at present, the overwhelming speed of

scientific and technological progress has transformed a static society into a highly dynamic one, marginalizing those no longer able to acquire new skills and knowledge. Experts in geriatrics suggest a mentally alert and physically active life as an antidote to the pitfalls of old age. While recognizing the value of health at all stages, the last one in particular, Rita adamantly believed that success in this context lay in understanding the inner mechanisms of the brain, which she considered far superior to any sophisticated computer because of its human awareness.

In more than one interview, Rita revealed the secret of her excellent physical and mental health. She took a lot of vitamin C and ate very little, once a day, for lunch, while in the evening she would have broth and fruit. Rita serenely accepted the marks of time on her body, but her mental faculties had never been compromised. She did not hide her hearing aids and she was not embarrassed that her eyes could hardly see. She maintained that while the years of her childhood were not happy, the years of her adolescence were good and the ones of her old age were the best. "What matters," she used to say, "is not the chronological age but the results, the style of life."

Even in her late nineties Rita kept the enthusiasm of her twenties; she wrote extensively, always fighting the commonplace view deeply rooted since Roman times: *Senectus morbus est* ("Old age is an illness"). And she spoke at several conferences on this topic, revising and constantly scientifically updating her approach. Indro Montanelli, journalist and historian, who was born on the same day and in the same year as Rita, envied her entrenched optimism. He had mixed feelings about old age, even though he kept writing as a significant witness of many major events of the twentieth century until late in life.

When Rita turned ninety, she was interviewed by journalist Enzo Biagi, who asked when a person should be considered "old." She answered: "Never, if the person wills it." In her opinion, everything depends on us, and the kind of country we live in. She added: "In a developing country, old age does not exist because most elderly people are integrated and feel useful to society; in the West, especially in the United States, where beauty is highly valued, one is old at around fifty; in a free country like Italy, where there are not too many preconceptions, old age does not exist. I am ninety. I am in my 'fourth age,' but this does not represent a burden for me. My brain still works." Rita kept a strong conviction that the brain, in spite of aging, maintains formidable renewal strategies and an intrinsic plasticity. She found that studying even on the threshold of the first century of life is possible and useful.[156]

Old age, the most dreaded and often miserable phase of human life, should be, for those free from undue hardship, a grand time, when one is finally free from worry and can enjoy life. Rita recommended that we should diversify our interests so that when we retire, we discover that life is not over, but rather that we are embarking on a new stage as productive as the previous ones.

Rita was so convinced about the necessity of working that in 2001 she upset quite a number of trade union representatives by maintaining that, in most cases, going into retirement marks the end of life, therefore "it should be abolished." Of course, she was not considering the often-brutal consequences of a life of hard physical labor. Rita never retired because she thought older people should not be treated as passive subjects, but should constantly involve themselves in life in the most varied possible ways.

Rita's book *L'asso nella manica a brandelli* is therefore a seminal textbook allowing readers to plan, possibly from a young age, to successfully cope with the final stage of life by becoming aware of the vital cerebral structures and functions. Since undoubtedly many more people will live longer in the years to come, this is surely pertinent advice.

Rita used the brilliant image of the ace of spades as the redeeming feature of old age, the indomitable belief in the power of the brain, and its continuous metamorphosis. It is the most spiritual card in the deck of life, the symbol of ancient mysteries, including the sacred science of playing cards. It represents transformation, faith in others, forgiveness, and unconditional love.

Rita thought that old age, if lived well, is worthy of respect and not of pity. However, she went one step further. Who can now have such a card up the sleeve, if for centuries it was available only to the privileged members of the aristocracy, clergy, and high bourgeoisie? Rita maintained that in the third millennium, the ace can be up everyone's sleeve, including those of women and people of any gender or class. It is no longer a privilege.

She scientifically supported her thesis by quoting Boston senior neurologist Dennis J. Selkoe, who believed that though the human brain in later life undergoes a loss of neurons and can suffer biochemical alterations, these changes in many individuals do not provoke a significant decline of the cognitive and creative faculties.[157] She also valued the considerations of mathematician Ennio De Giorgi from the *Scuola Normale Superiore*, Pisa, who, while acknowledging one's limits, believed that the cells in the brains of elderly people can find alternative ways to increase and revitalize cerebral circuits, so that they can still use and enjoy their mental faculties.

Interestingly enough, Rita thought that later in life her imagination and creativity had substantially improved, and that was a reassuring discovery, confirming Einstein's conviction that imagination is even more important than knowledge. Not only that, but in her nineties she was still consumed with curiosity and the spirit of adventure, echoing Marie Curie, who, also late in life, wrote: "I am one of those who think that science has great beauty. Scholars in the laboratory are not just technicians; they are also children, face to face with natural phenomena that impress them like a fairy tale."[158] On the way to one hundred, Rita felt free more than ever to candidly describe her life as a honeymoon with the brain.

When she was ninety-nine, she went to Israel and met eight young scientists from different parts of the world. The girls sat informally on the lawn of the campus while she preferred to sit on a chair among them. She spoke about scientific research, and the undervalued intelligence of women, while willingly answering all kinds of questions. She was proud to say, "I went my way," referring to her decision, early in life, not to become a wife and a mother. She reiterated the importance of being consistent with one's principles without ever forgetting to help anyone in need.

Asked if, in spite of her successful life, she had any regrets, her answer was "No, never!" With the same energy she asserted that every calamity could be transformed into an opportunity. She was such an incorrigible optimist that she even maintained that ultimately the racial laws had proven to be a blessing in disguise for her. She had built a small lab in her bedroom, shutting out any distraction from her academic life, and pursued the research that led to the discovery of NGF.

She reached over a century of life with great inner strength. She was aware that she could not see or hear well, but she declared, "Now I think more than in my twenties. The body can do what it likes. I am not the body: I am the mind. And when the body dies, what survives is what you have done, the message you have given."[159]

The death of Renato Dulbecco, on a cold February day in 2012, reminded her of an equally frigid winter day when Salvador Luria died in 1991. Of the magic trio from Turin, she was the only survivor. Renato's death, however, undeniably compromised Rita's physical and mental energy, as if her lifelong friend and colleague had carried with him the memories of their past as well as the hopes and dreams that she still possessed.

Until the end of her life, nonetheless, she was driven almost every day to the European Brain Research Institute in her Alfa Romeo with a car phone and lived in a whirlwind of appointments. Promoting Italian science wherever she went, she kept two secretaries, one who worked in English and the other in Italian. She often even visited elementary and secondary schools because Rita loved children very much and believed it was never too early to engage them. She was loved by everybody, rarely criticized, revered as a celebrity—a unique achievement for a scientist. It is not surprising that over seventy schools were named after her from the north to the south of Italy.

On December 30, 2012, Rita died in her cherished Roman apartment, comforted by the people she loved. The previous day, the last person she received was her close collaborator Luigi Aloe. She was sitting in her armchair and looked more small and frail than ever in her blue dress. As he was about to leave, she raised her hand to keep him a little longer and asked, "Luigi, please, tell me what is the latest on NGF?" She was almost one hundred and four. A few hours later, she would close her eyes forever, but her thirst for knowledge was still unquenched.

Her death was announced by the national and international press and widely commented on by social media and TV for days on end. The casket with her body was brought to the Senate of the Italian Republic where, for hours thousands of people silently lined up to pay tribute to a woman who had encompassed the history of the twentieth century and the beginning of the third millennium.

After learning the sad news from Rita's niece Piera, Giorgio Napolitano, the president of the Italian Republic, paid tribute to Rita Levi-Montalcini as "a luminous figure in the history of science, honoring Italy, as well as a symbol marking the civic integration of women in society." She had followed in the footsteps of the great scientists of the past, from Charles Darwin to Albert Einstein, from Marie Curie to Maria Montessori. The

European Brain Research Institute remains a tangible mark of her legacy.

A few days later, she was buried in the family tomb that her brother had designed in the Monumental Cemetery of Turin. But she was not there. She was not the body. She was the mind, and she still lives on in the values she left us.

Epilogue

THE LEGACY OF RITA LEVI-MONTALCINI

Life does not end with death. What you pass on to others remains. Immortality is not the body, which one day will die. That does not matter. What does matter is the message you leave to others. That is immortality.

—RITA LEVI-MONTALCINI

Rita was a scientist and an innovator, but above all, she was a freethinker and a feminist. Only at the age of twenty did she find the inner strength to assert her intellectual independence by challenging all the Jewish cultural norms that at the time confined a woman to the roles of daughter, wife, and mother. She tore down cultural walls within her own patriarchal family and became the first female among the Levi-Montalcinis to earn a degree in Medicine and Surgery, graduating summa cum laude. A late bloomer, she needed determination and commitment to reach her goals. After she emerged from a painfully shy adolescence, she counted strongly on the interaction of equally motivated friends or partners to share her aspirations and efforts. By studying for months, day and night, with her cousin Eugenia, she managed to pass the difficult exam that allowed her access to the academic milieu.

This proved to be a real turning point. At the university, though Rita was older than most of her colleagues, she had a very positive collaboration with Salvador Luria and Renato Dulbecco, without ever thinking that fifty-seven years later, she would receive a Nobel Prize, as did the two of them. She truly considered herself a Cinderella of science until she reached the age of forty, but always welcomed the opportunity to meet other scientists and Nobel Prize winners, whose company she found scientifically and culturally enriching.

She was fortunate enough to also have two very special mentors who helped her immensely to forge her professional life, and with whom she developed a deep, meaningful friendship: Giuseppe Levi at the University of Turin and Viktor Hamburger at Washington University in St. Louis. The former gave her an excellent training in histology while the latter offered her a fellowship of six months at Washington University, which then turned into a thirty-year position in the US—her whole university career.

No difficulty put her down, not even the 1938 racial laws enforced under Benito Mussolini; paradoxically, they determined her true direction in life. By bravely choosing to stay in Italy with her family risking deportation, Rita, by then a scientist in her own right—though rejected by society and without a job—found great comfort in the life of the mind.

The outbreak of the Second World War left a deep mark on her; she generated enough antibodies and developed the necessary resilience to remain a convinced fighter while spitefully working in hiding. Moreover, she found in Giuseppe Levi a unique ally in her initially solitary battle. Her former professor, who shared the same destiny of a persecuted Jew, taught her the secrets of research with fatherly care.

While in the sinister atmosphere of fascist Italy many people lived paralyzed with fear and hatred, Rita managed to shape her own future and take constructive steps forward as a neuroscientist through her ability to focus unwaveringly on work, despite the destruction that surrounded her.

Emotionally unequipped to be a practicing medical doctor, she became interested in exploring and understanding how nature works, in particular the most mysterious of our organs: the brain. However, since science evolves continually and new discoveries endlessly open fresh perspectives, she was intellectually eager to refocus on what other scientists had already explored before her, in order to reach new ways of understanding. This brought her in 1947 to work with her new mentor, Viktor Hamburger, at Washington University.

When Rita started her research on the nervous system, her field of interest did not seem to have any relevant future and she had to fight her way through constant ups and downs. Only in North America, thanks to the authority and encouragement of Salvador Luria, did all her doubts finally vanish. In Italy, she had to overcome all kinds of prejudice and discrimination—being a woman, a Jew, and a scientist—while in the States she felt immediately free. Once she arrived in St. Louis at the age of thirty-eight, hardly knowing the language, she was able to disentangle from all the preconceptions of the Old World and blossom as a scientist. Away from the authoritarian presence of Levi, she could unbridle her imagination, reinvent herself, and work to her heart's content.

At Washington University—which she considered the Promised Land of Science, where merit was generously rewarded and an adequate salary was granted—she experienced a priceless sense of empowerment and responsibility. Her choice not to have a family of her own gave her the flexibility she wanted, helping her champion a different perception of women in the medical and scientific sector. Her research work was never intended as a tedious nine-to-five job, but as an irrepressible vocation and a galvanizing adventure that would need a whole lifetime, and beyond, to express itself.

From the very beginning Rita approached science chiefly from an artistic point of view, as she often stated, and found in it a sense of wonder and beauty. After all, her mother, Adele, and her twin sister, Paola, were painters; her brother, Gino, a sculptor and architect. She was proud to come from a family of artists and therefore described herself as "an artist on loan to science." Art, literature, music, history, and philosophy always found space in her humanistic existence as a university student and, later on, as a successful scientist and professor. She was convinced that any scientific finding was the result not so much of a mere diligent assembly and elaboration of information, but rather of special intuitions fostered by a gratifying creative life.

She made every difficulty work in her favor, including Missouri's frigid winters because they created the ideal conditions for her to focus on research, without any major distractions. Moreover, she thought that "in scientific research, neither the degree of one's intelligence nor the ability to carry out one's tasks with thoroughness and precision are factors essential to personal success and fulfillment. More important . . . are total dedication and a tendency to underestimate difficulties, which cause one to tackle problems that other more critical and acute persons, instead, opt to avoid."[160]

Rita had deliberately entered the world of science as a pioneer. As such, she was eager to try new approaches, push boundaries, face new challenges. She was happy and excited to experiment and verify other scholars' accomplishments or intuitions. Now being in the New World where everything was possible, she aimed with even greater dedication at being recognized as a scientist herself, and gradually, almost without realizing it, gained a place on the international scientific platform. Often she was the only woman participating in scientific panels traditionally reserved for men, as had happened to Marie Curie in Europe. And this gave her a growing sense of gratification and pride.[161]

She was already becoming renowned in scientific circles, but her forte was recognizing her own limits. The humble awareness of not knowing enough was her guiding star: a constant invitation to keep searching, learning, and going beyond the given facts.

After her meticulous in vitro investigation at the Institute of Biophysics in Rio de Janeiro, she knew she needed a talented biochemist to make major strides forward in her research. With Stanley Cohen, her new associate over the next six exciting and intense years in St. Louis, she discovered the mysterious factor or protein molecule, which finally received the name of nerve growth factor, or NGF. This initiated an unprecedented revolution in neuroscience, which granted Rita and Stanley the Nobel Prize in 1986.

Her discovery, identification, and isolation of NGF ultimately resulted in a major leap forward in the research field of developmental neurobiology, but for years she was not entirely aware of the great promise it held in the treatment of central nervous system diseases.

Rita never stopped dreaming and working hard at the same time, proving to be a real visionary and making the impossible possible. After thirty years in America, she eventually returned to Italy, eager to be close to her family and to bring her own experience to the Italian scientific milieu. So she bravely became a pioneer once again, but in her own country: She was simultaneously directing the new Research Center for Neurobiology—initially located in one room in a basement in the historic center of Rome—and her state-of-the-art lab in St. Louis. She became a valuable scientific ambassador by creating a bridge for research and innovation between two continents.

This was not enough for the expanding visionary plans that

she had in mind, and which she pursued with undiminished perseverance and conviction. She fulfilled her lifelong aspiration to leave a permanent mark on the international scientific scene by founding in Rome, at the age of ninety-two, the European Brain Research Institute (EBRI). This way she provided new space and opportunities to young talents from all walks of life, so that they could dedicate themselves to scientific investigation and experimentation.

EBRI has gradually become a leading center for research on the brain and neurodegenerative diseases, such as Alzheimer's, Parkinson's, Huntington's, and ALS. It is significant that Rita maintained that the most precious organ of our body is gifted with enormous potential for alertness, creativity, and productivity—on the condition that it is kept constantly exercised.

By believing in the persisting vitality and adaptability of the brain, she gave a new dignity to old age, the most dreaded stage of human life. Her new, updated scientific interpretation challenged popular misconceptions regarding the aging mind and debunked common demeaning myths associated with it. At the same time, she never stopped interacting with young people because she believed in the importance of an intergenerational exchange, and thought the future belonged to the young.

Rita actually managed to train a new generation of scientists, fighting against nepotism, favoritism, and political pressure while embracing the values of freedom and democracy and serving individual institutions with loyalty. Throughout her life, she demonstrated deep commitment to transmitting not only knowledge, but also values. She taught that science cannot be subservient to any ideology because it should be at the service of humankind and not vice versa. Research should be free, but guided by ethical principles and international norms.

Rita had such a deep respect for the problems afflicting adolescents that she urged them, either in person or through a number of publications, to be actors rather than spectators on the world stage by finding the right path for their professional life. She wanted to spare them the same hardships and painful doubts that she had experienced when she was young.

For Rita, life and science were one, and her civic engagement increasingly became a moral call, so that she spent the last two decades of her life mainly pursuing three socially oriented objectives. First, to fight illiteracy at all levels. Second, to help young people realize their potential. Third, to empower women, eradicating discrimination against them and making sure that—even in developing countries—they all had the same great privilege she had experienced: access to education. Rita knew that radical change was needed for the sake of global society as a whole, in order to cope with the technological, economic, and political change brought by the third millennium.

In a tumultuous world threatened by nuclear weapons, religious and racial prejudice, global warming, hunger, organized crime, and child abuse, it was now time, she thought, not only to call for rights, but also for duties. She believed that a new solidarity was needed as well as international collaboration to dismiss once and for all destructive weapons of any kind, and finally generate a commitment to improve the quality of life on the entire planet. The threat of new discoveries in the field of neurobiology leading to the possible creation of pharmacological weapons, no less dangerous than the atomic ones, should be counterbalanced by the international community setting the rules of the game.

Rita fully endorsed Albert Einstein's acknowledgment of the high responsibility of scientists. She was convinced that she and her colleagues had to complement their research in the lab by involving themselves with social issues in order to increase awareness of the most urgent concerns of humankind. She regularly quoted Einstein: "We scientists have to think in a different way from the others, if we want society to improve. We make an appeal as human beings: remember your humanity, the rest does not count."[162]

When appointed a life senator of the Italian Republic, she finally had a chance to realize this message and make it count. She was the second woman in the history of the country to obtain this coveted title and thus became even more of a living legend, an exemplary role model to all other women.

I had the privilege of meeting Rita Levi-Montalcini at the Ministry of Foreign Affairs in Rome in the year 2000, before being posted to Chicago and then to Los Angeles. She was in her early nineties and yet she was elegant, eloquent, full of ideas and proposals that she generously expressed to a selected group of directors of Italian Cultural Institutes. I was struck by her generous availability, physical and mental vitality, and wit.

Born a woman in a man's world, Rita rose to a level of accomplishment that very few people ever achieve. Thanks to her visionary nature and to the positive thinking that guided her life, she persisted in a scientifically undervalued field, and overcame unimaginable hardships. She trusted her intuition when others, including her cherished mentor, dismissed it. Through the years she has become a symbol of hope, courage, and strength. Her example can indeed give young people the confidence to face the challenges of life.

Exemplifying William Butler Yeats's belief that "in dreams begins responsibility," she managed to fulfill each important dream of her life, and took concrete steps to enable others, less privileged than herself, to realize their own potential. "After all," Rita once observed, "what matters is not so much reality but our dreams."[163]

Appendix A

Rita Levi-Montalcini's Acceptance Speech
The Nobel Banquet
December 10, 1986

Your Majesties, Your Royal Highnesses, Ladies and Gentlemen,

It is with very deep emotion that my dear friend Stanley Cohen and I stand here today, in front of you, and wish to express our immense gratitude for having been bestowed with the greatest honor that a scientist can ever dream of receiving for his or her accomplishments: the Nobel Prize.

Stanley and I first began to work together thirty-three years ago in the Department of Zoology of the Washington University in St. Louis, Missouri, chaired at the time by Professor Viktor Hamburger, a leading scientist in Experimental Neuroembryology, a great scholar and a most beloved master and friend. Since then, we enjoyed every minute of this adventure which was to lead us to Stockholm.

Stanley's exceptional talent and most rigorous training in

biochemistry, and my own training in neurology, which I had the privilege of receiving from the famous Italian scientist, the late Giuseppe Levi, at the Medical School of the University of Turin, provided us with an ideal complementary background to tackle what at first seemed a fairly easy puzzle to solve: namely, to uncover the nature and mechanism of action of a protein molecule which became known, on account of its biological properties, as the "Nerve Growth Factor." It took, however, more than three decades to realize the complexity of the problem which is at present still under intensive investigation all over the world.

I wish to add that while Stanley devoted from 1961 to the present day all his skills and expertise in exploring another growth factor, the Epidermal Growth Factor, in the Department of Biochemistry of the University in Nashville, Tennessee, I was most fortunate to be joined twenty years ago by Professor Pietro Calissano and Luigi Aloe, two outstanding investigators and dearest friends, who worked daily with me or independently and to whom goes most of the merit for the success in our recent studies of Nerve Growth Factor.

As far as I am concerned, I must add that Nerve Growth Factor would perhaps never have been discovered were it not for the rigorous neurobiological training which I received in my native country, at the University of Turin, and of the most generous hospitality and invaluable scientific and technical help which I received at Washington University, where I spent the thirty happiest and most productive years of my life.

To our Swedish colleagues and dear friends, I wish to express my everlasting gratitude for their fundamental contributions in the field of Neurosciences. To them we all are indebted for having opened the gates of the golden era in the field of neurobiology, and I personally feel, even more than anybody else, thankful for their outstanding work in the area of Nerve Growth Factor.

Appendix B

Autobiography by Rita Levi-Montalcini
Prepared for the Nobel Foundation
December 1986

My twin sister Paola and I were born in Turin on April 22, 1909, the youngest of four children. Our parents were Adamo Levi, an electrical engineer and gifted mathematician, and Adele Montalcini, a talented painter and an exquisite human being. Our older brother Gino, who died twelve years ago of a heart attack, was one of the most well-known Italian architects and a professor at the University of Turin. Our sister Anna, five years older than Paola and myself, lives in Turin with her children and grandchildren. Ever since adolescence, she has been an enthusiastic admirer of the great Swedish writer, the Nobel Laureate Selma Lagerlöf, and she infected me so much with her enthusiasm that I decided to become a writer and describe an Italian saga "à la Lagerlöf." But things were to take a different turn.

The four of us enjoyed a most wonderful family atmosphere,

filled with love and reciprocal devotion. Both parents were highly cultured and instilled in us their high appreciation of intellectual pursuit. It was, however, a typical Victorian style of life, all decisions being taken by the head of the family, the husband and father. He loved us dearly and had a great respect for women, but he believed that a professional career would interfere with the duties of a wife and mother. He therefore decided that the three of us—Anna, Paola and I—would not engage in studies which open the way to a professional career and that we would not enroll in the University.

Ever since childhood, Paola had shown an extraordinary artistic talent and father's decision did not prevent her full-time dedication to painting. She became one of the most outstanding women painters in Italy and is at present still in full activity. I had a more difficult time; at twenty, I realized that I could not possibly adjust to a feminine role as conceived by my father, and asked him permission to engage in a professional career. In eight months I filled my gaps in Latin, Greek and mathematics, graduated from high school, and entered medical school in Turin. Two of my university colleagues and close friends, Salvador Luria and Renato Dulbecco, were to receive the Nobel Prize in Physiology or Medicine, respectively, seventeen and eleven years before I would receive the same most prestigious award. All three of us were students of the famous Italian histologist, Giuseppe Levi. We are indebted to him for a superb training in biological science, and for having learned to approach scientific problems in a most rigorous way at a time when such an approach was still unusual.

In 1936 I graduated from medical school with a summa cum laude degree in Medicine and Surgery, and enrolled in the three-year specialization in neurology and psychiatry, still uncertain whether I should devote myself fully to the medical profession or pursue at the same time basic research in neurology. My perplexity was not to last too long.

In 1936 Mussolini issued the "Manifesto per la Difesa della Razza," signed by ten Italian "scientists." The manifesto was soon followed by the promulgation of laws barring academic and professional careers to non-Aryan Italian citizens. After a short period spent in Brussels as a guest of a neurological institute, I returned to Turin on the verge of the invasion of Belgium by the German army, Spring 1940, to join my family. The two alternatives left then to us were either to emigrate to the United States, or to pursue some activity that needed neither support nor connection with the outside Aryan world where we lived. My family chose this second alternative. I then decided to build a small research unit at home and installed it in my bedroom. My inspiration was a 1934 article by Viktor Hamburger reporting on the effects of limb extirpation in chick embryos. My project had barely started when Giuseppe Levi, who had escaped from Belgium invaded by Nazis, returned to Turin and joined me, thus becoming, to my great pride, my first and only assistant.

The heavy bombing of Turin by Anglo-American air forces in 1941 made it imperative to abandon Turin and move to a country cottage where I rebuilt my mini-laboratory and resumed my experiments. In the fall of 1943, the invasion of Italy by the

German army forced us to abandon our now dangerous refuge in Piemonte and flee to Florence, where we lived underground until the end of the war.

In Florence I was in daily contact with many close, dear friends and courageous partisans of the "Partito di Azione." In August of 1944, the advancing Anglo-American armies forced the German invaders to leave Florence. At the Anglo-American Headquarters, I was hired as a medical doctor and assigned to a camp of war refugees who were brought to Florence by the hundreds from the North where the war was still raging. Epidemics of infectious diseases and of abdominal typhus spread death among the refugees, of whom I was in charge as nurse and medical doctor, sharing with them their suffering and the daily danger of death.

The war in Italy ended in May 1945. I returned with my family to Turin where I resumed my academic positions at the University. In the Fall of 1947, an invitation from Professor Viktor Hamburger to join him and repeat the experiments which he had performed many years earlier on chick embryos was to change the course of my life.

Although I had planned to remain in St. Louis for only ten to twelve months, the excellent results of our research made it imperative for me to postpone my return to Italy. In 1956 I was offered the position of Associate Professor and in 1958 that of Full Professor, a position which I held until retirement in 1977. In 1962 I established a research unit in Rome, dividing my time between this city and St. Louis. From 1969 to 1978 I also held the position of Director of the Institute of Cell Biology of the Italian National Council of Research, in Rome. Upon retirement in 1979, I became Guest Professor of this same institute.

Appendix C

Alfred Bernhard Nobel was born in Stockholm, Sweden, on October 21, 1833, but spent most of his youth in St. Petersburg, Russia, where his father introduced him to the family trade: manufacturing explosives. His family had descended from Olof Rudbeck, the best-known technical genius in seventeenth-century Sweden.

Working in the family business outside Stockholm, he helped develop a chemical combination of nitroglycerine and gunpowder, used to blast out earth for building roads, canals, and tunnels. The explosive, however, was unpredictable and Alfred Nobel felt guilty when his family's product killed innocent workers. He was determined to design a safer explosive: dynamite.

His invention made him millions. When he died in 1896, his family members were shocked to learn that he had left all his fortune to establish a foundation that would award prizes to individuals from all over the world whose work had made the greatest contributions to human progress. He designated that prizes should be awarded in five areas—Peace, Literature, Physics, Chemistry, and Physiology or Medicine—and later, Economics.

Nobel Prize winners receive a medal and a significant monetary award, the amount of which fluctuates according to the interest earned by the original Nobel investment.

The first winner of the Nobel Prize for Physiology or Medicine was Emil von Behring, a German doctor and professor of hygiene whose discoveries led to immunizations against diphtheria and tuberculosis. In 2003, Paul Lauterbur of Urbana, Illinois, and Sir Peter Mansfield of Nottingham, England, shared their prize for their work on magnetic resonance imaging.

The Nobel Prize in Physiology or Medicine was more recently awarded to Richard Axel and Linda B. Buck "for their discoveries of odorant receptors and the organization of the olfactory system" (2004); Barry J. Marshall and J. Robin Warren "for their discovery of the bacterium *Helicobacter pylori* and its role in gastritis and peptic ulcer disease" (2005); Andrew Z. Fire and Craig C. Mello "for their discovery of RNA interference—gene silencing by double-stranded RNA" (2006); Mario R. Capecchi, Sir Martin J. Evans, and Oliver Smithies "for their discoveries of principles for introducing specific gene modifications in mice by the use of embryonic stem cells" (2007); Harald zur Hausen "for his discovery of human papilloma viruses causing cervical cancer" as well as Françoise Barré-Sinoussi and Luc Montagnier "for their discovery of human immunodeficiency virus" (2008);

Elizabeth H. Blackburn, Carol W. Greider, and Jack W. Szostak "for the discovery of how chromosomes are protected by telomeres and the enzyme telomerase" (2009); Robert G. Edwards "for the development of in vitro fertilization" (2010); Bruce A. Beutler and Jules A. Hoffmann "for their discoveries concerning the activation of innate immunity" as well as Ralph M. Steinman "for his discovery of the dendritic cell and its role in adaptive immunity" (2011); Sir John B. Gurdon and Shinya Yamanaka "for the discovery that mature cells can be reprogrammed to become pluripotent" (2012); James E. Rothman, Randy W. Schekman, and Thomas C. Südhof "for their discoveries of machinery regulating vesicle traffic, a major transport system in our cells" (2013); John O'Keefe, May-Britt Moser, and Edvard I. Moser "for their discoveries of cells that constitute a positioning system in the brain" (2014); William C. Campbell and Satoshi Ōmura "for their discoveries concerning a new therapy against infections caused by roundworm parasites" as well as Tu Youyou "for her discoveries concerning a novel therapy against Malaria" (2015); Yoshinori Ohsumi "for his discoveries of mechanisms for autophagy" (2016); Jeffrey C. Hall, Michael Rosbash, and Michael W. Young "for their discoveries of molecular mechanisms controlling the circadian rhythm" (2017); James P. Allison and Tasuku Honjo "for their discovery of cancer therapy by inhibition of negative immune regulation" (2018); William G. Kaelin Jr., Sir Peter J. Ratcliffe, and Gregg L. Semenza "for their discoveries of how cells sense and adapt to oxygen availability" (2019); and Harvey J. Alter, Michael Houghton, and Charles M. Rice "for the discovery of Hepatitis C virus" (2020).

Notes

PROLOGUE: THE NOBEL PRIZE, DECEMBER 10, 1986

1. Rita Levi Montalcini, *Cantico di una vita* (Milan: Raffaello Cortina Editore, 2000), 59.
2. Rita Levi-Montalcini, with an essay by Elena Cattaneo, *NGF, La molecola della vita* (Rome: Treccani, 2019), 39.
3. Levi-Montalcini, *Cantico di una vita*, 156.
4. Susan Tyler Hitchcock, *Rita Levi-Montalcini: Nobel Prize Winner* (Philadelphia: Chelsea House Publishers, 2005), 95.
5. Rita Levi-Montalcini, *In Praise of Imperfection: My Life and Work* (New York: Basic Books Inc., 1988), 200.
6. The Nobel Assembly at the Karolinska Institute, "The Nobel Prize in Physiology or Medicine 1986," Press Release, October 13, 1986, https://www.nobelprize.org/prizes/medicine/1986/press-release/.
7. Luigi Garlando, in conversation with Luigi Aloe, *Mosche, cavallette, scarafaggi e premio Nobel* (Milan: Harper Collins, 2019), 10–11, 222–227.

8. Paolo Giordano, "Cento anni di futuro. Intervista a Rita Levi Montalcini," *Wired*, February 19, 2000.

9. Cristiana Pulcinelli and Tina Simoniello, *Rita Levi-Montalcini* (Rome: L'asino d'oro edizioni, 2014), 16–17.

CHAPTER ONE: GROWING UP IN A JEWISH FAMILY IN TURIN

10. Lisa Yount, *Rita Levi-Montalcini: Discoverer of Nerve Growth Factor* (New York: Chelsea House Publishers, 2009), 4.

11. Rita Levi-Montalcini, *Senz'olio contro vento* (Milan: Baldini Castoldi, 1996), 121.

12. Levi-Montalcini, *In Praise of Imperfection*, 25.

13. Ibid., 33.

14. Rita Levi-Montalcini, with Giuseppina Tripodi, *Rita Levi-Montalcini racconta la scuola ai ragazzi* (Milan: Fabbri Editori, 2007), 20.

CHAPTER TWO: REBELLING AGAINST A PATRIARCHAL SOCIETY

15. John Ruskin, *Sesame and Lilies* (London: Dent, 1907), 59–60.

16. Levi-Montalcini, *In Praise of Imperfection*, 30.

17. Ibid., 31.

18. Ibid., 11.

19. Ibid., 37.

20. Rita Levi-Montalcini, *Tempo di mutamenti* (Milan: Baldini Castoldi, 2002), 20.

21. Ibid., 86.

22. Ibid., 64.

23. Sigmund Freud, *Psicoanalisi della società moderna* (Rome: Newton Compton Editori, 2018), 42.

24. Levi-Montalcini, *In Praise of Imperfection*, 46.

CHAPTER THREE: THE CLASSES OF GIUSEPPE LEVI

25. Natalia Ginzburg, *Lessico famigliare* (Turin: Einaudi, 1963), 13.

26. Levi-Montalcini, *In Praise of Imperfection*, 52.

27. Ginzburg, *Lessico famigliare*, 3.

28. Levi-Montalcini, *In Praise of Imperfection*, 62.

29. Paola Capriolo, *Rita Levi-Montalcini. Una vita per la conoscenza* (San Dorligo della Valle (TS): Edizioni EL, 2017), 22.

30. Rita Levi-Montalcini, *Elogio dell'imperfezione* (Milan: Garzanti, 1987), 65.

31. Ginzburg, *Lessico famigliare*, 74.

32. Yount, *Rita Levi-Montalcini: Discoverer of Nerve Growth Factor*, 14.

33. Levi-Montalcini, *In Praise of Imperfection*, 126.

34. Ibid., 60.

CHAPTER FOUR: THE RISE OF FASCISM AND THE ANTI-SEMITIC LAWS

35. Renzo De Felice, *The Jews in Fascist Italy: A History* (New York: Enigma Books, 2015), 64.

36. Elsa Morante, *History* (New York: Alfred Knopf, 1977), 6.

37. Pulcinelli and Simoniello, *Rita Levi-Montalcini*, 40.

38. Ginzburg, *Lessico famigliare*, 103.

39. Ibid., 96.

40. De Felice, *The Jews in Fascist Italy*, 148.

41. Ibid., 10.

42. Ibid., 458.

43. Levi-Montalcini, *In Praise of Imperfection*, 80.

44. William Butler Yeats, edited by Roberto Sanesi, "*The Second Coming*," *Poesie* (Milan: Lerici Ed., 1961), 266.

45. Levi-Montalcini, *In Praise of Imperfection*, 83.

46. De Felice, *The Jews in Fascist Italy*, 346.

47. Morante, *History*, 46.

48. R.D.L. September 7, 1938, n. 1390, 22-27.

49. De Felice, *The Jews in Fascist Italy*, 10.

50. Ibid., 327–328.

51. Ibid., 385.

CHAPTER FIVE: A LAB IN THE BEDROOM

52. Ibid., 413.

53. Antonio Gramsci, *Note sul Machiavelli, sulla politica e sullo stato moderno* (Turin: Einaudi, 1949), 238.

54. Levi-Montalcini, *In Praise of Imperfection*, 89.

55. Dante Alighieri, *La Divina Commedia, Inferno*, canto XXVI, translated by Elio Zappulla (New York: Pantheon Books, 1998), 233.

56. Levi-Montalcini, *In Praise of Imperfection*, 90.

57. Ginzburg, *Lessico famigliare*, 157.

58. Ibid., 163.

59. Levi-Montalcini, *In Praise of Imperfection*, 91.

60. Yount, Rita Levi-Montalcini: *Discoverer of Nerve Growth Factor*, 27.

61. Levi-Montalcini, *In Praise of Imperfection*, 95.

62. De Felice, *The Jews in Fascist Italy*, 359.

63. Galeazzo Ciano, *Diario 1939–43* (Milan: Rizzoli, 1947), 158.

64. Yeats, "*The Second Coming*," *Poesie*, 266.

65. Pietro Badoglio, *L'Italia nella seconda guerra mondiale* (Milan: Mondadori, 1946), 92.

66. Capriolo, *Rita Levi-Montalcini. Una vita per la conoscenza*, 35.

67. Levi-Montalcini, *In Praise of Imperfection*, 102.

68. Yount, *Rita Levi-Montalcini: Discoverer of Nerve Growth Factor*, 39.

69. De Felice, *The Jews in Fascist Italy*, 448.

70. De Felice, *The Jews in Fascist Italy*, 461.

71. Ibid., 457.

72. Levi-Montalcini, *Senz'olio contro vento*, 110.

73. Primo Levi, *Se questo è un uomo* (Turin: Einaudi, 1945), 38.

74. Levi-Montalcini, *Senz'olio contro vento*, 128.

75. Ibid., 132.

76. Ginzburg, *Lessico famigliare*, 139.

77. Ibid., 198.

78. Yount, *Rita Levi-Montalcini: Discoverer of Nerve Growth Factor*, 40.

79. Levi-Montalcini, *In Praise of Imperfection*, 111.

CHAPTER SIX: CROSSING THE ATLANTIC

80. Manfredi Toraldo and Francesco Mobili, *Rita Levi-Montalcini. A Pioneer in Neuroscience*, curated by Senato della Repubblica

and Fondazione EBRI Rita Levi-Montalcini, translation by Pina Moliterno, 2016, 19.

81. Levi-Montalcini, *In Praise of Imperfection*, 185.

82. Fred Samson, *The Neurosciences: Paths of Discovery II* (Boston: Birkhäuser, 1992), 329.

CHAPTER SEVEN: RESEARCH YEARS IN ST. LOUIS

83. Rita Levi-Montalcini, with Giuseppina Tripodi, *Le tue antenate. Donne pioniere nella società e nella scienza dall'antichità ai giorni nostri* (Rome: Gallucci, 2008), 119.

84. Yount, *Rita Levi-Montalcini: Discoverer of Nerve Growth Factor*, 49.

85. Ibid., 51.

86. Levi-Montalcini, *In Praise of Imperfection*, 135.

87. Levi-Montalcini, *Cantico di una vita*, 270.

88. Rita Levi-Montalcini, *Un universo inquieto* (Milan: Baldini Castoldi, 2001), 255.

89. Levi-Montalcini, *In Praise of Imperfection*, p. 141.

90. Ibid., 142.

CHAPTER EIGHT: THE DISCOVERY OF NERVE GROWTH FACTOR

91. Elmer Bueker, "Implantation of tumors in the hind limb field of the embryonic chick and the developmental response of the lumbosacral embryonic chick and the developmental response of the lumbosacral nervous system," *Anatomical Record*, 1948: 369–390.

92. Levi-Montalcini, *In Praise of Imperfection*, 146.

93. Rita Levi-Montalcini, *Cronologia di una scoperta* (Milan: Baldini Castoldi, 2009), 44.

94. Rita Levi-Montalcini, *Abbi il coraggio di conoscere* (Milan: Rizzoli, 2004), 119–121.

95. Salvador Luria, "Storia della biologia molecolare," *Letture Nobel* (Milan: Montedison-Progetto cultura), 1987, 57.

96. Levi-Montalcini, *In Praise of Imperfection*, 148.

97. Pietro Calissano, *Rita Levi-Montalcini. La vita fra i neuroni* (Florence: Edizioni Clichy, 2017), 20.

98. Levi-Montalcini, *Cronologia di una scoperta*, 48.

99. *Hitchcock,* Rita Levi-Montalcini: Nobel Prize Winner, 64.

100. Levi-Montalcini, *In Praise of Imperfection*, 159.

101. Yount, *Rita Levi-Montalcini: Discoverer of Nerve Growth Factor*, 71.

102. Enrica Battifoglia, *Rita Levi-Montalcini. L'irresistibile fascino del cervello* (Milan: Hoepli, 2018), 73.

103. Levi-Montalcini, *In Praise of Imperfection*, 160.

104. Rita Levi-Montalcini, T*he Saga of the Nerve Growth Factor: Preliminary Studies, Discovery, Further Development* (River Edge, N.J., and London: World Scientific Publishing Company, 1997), vol. 3, 145–148.

105. Yount, *Rita Levi-Montalcini: Discoverer of Nerve Growth Factor*, 83.

106. Rita Levi-Montalcini, "NGF, An Unchartered Route," in Frederick G. Worden, Judith P. Swazey, and George Adelman, eds, *The Neurosciences: Paths of Discovery* (Cambridge, Mass., and London: MIT Press, 1975), 253.

107. Hitchcock, *Rita Levi-Montalcini: Nobel Prize Winner*, 72.

108. Levi-Montalcini, *In Praise of Imperfection*, 167.

CHAPTER NINE: COMMUTING BETWEEN THE USA AND ITALY

109. Ibid., 186.

110. Levi-Montalcini, *Senz'olio contro vento*, 13–28.

111. Yount, *Rita Levi-Montalcini: Discoverer of Nerve Growth Factor*, 87.

112. Levi-Montalcini, *In Praise of Imperfection*, 190.

113. Ibid., 191.

114. Ibid., 205.

115. Battifoglia, *Rita Levi-Montalcini. L'irresistibile fascino del cervello*, 86.

116. Ibid., 196.

117. Calissano, *Rita Levi-Montalcini. La vita fra i neuroni*, 22.

118. Salvador Edward Luria, *A Slot Machine, A Broken Test Tube: An Autobiography* (New York: Harper & Row, 1984), 42.

119. Sharon Bertsch McGrayne, *Nobel Prize Women in Science: Their Lives, Struggles, and Momentous Discoveries* (Washington, D.C.: Joseph Henry Press, 2001), 217.

120. Luigi Garlando, in conversation with Luigi Aloe, *Mosche, cavallette, scarafaggi e premio Nobel* (Milan: HarperCollins, 2019), 155.

121. Levi-Montalcini, *In Praise of Imperfection*, 196.

122. Samson, *The Neurosciences: Paths of Discovery*, 325.

123. Levi-Montalcini, *NGF, An Unchartered Route*, 261–262.

124. Yount, *Rita Levi-Montalcini: Discoverer of Nerve Growth Factor*, 97–100.

125. Calissano, *Rita Levi-Montalcini. La vita fra i neuroni*, 26.

126. Levi-Montalcini, *In Praise of Imperfection: My Life and Work*, 151.

CHAPTER TEN: A NEW LIFE IN ITALY

127. Levi-Montalcini, *Cronologia di una scoperta*, 42–47.

128. Kerstin Hall, Presentation Speech, Nobel Prize for Physiology or Medicine, 1986, https://www.nobelprize.org/prizes/medicine/1986/ceremony-speech/.

129. Calissano, *Rita Levi-Montalcini. La vita fra i neuroni*, 221.

130. Yount, *Rita Levi-Montalcini: Discoverer of Nerve Growth Factor*, 103.

131. Carola Vai, *Rita Levi-Montalcini. Una donna libera* (Soveria Mannelli: Rubbettino, 2019), 238.

CHAPTER ELEVEN: THE NOBEL PRIZE AND ITS IMPACT

132. Rita Levi-Montalcini, with Giuseppina Tripodi, *L'istruzione chiave dello sviluppo* (Milan: Baldini Castoldi Dalai, 1993), 199.

133. Levi-Montalcini, *La clessidra della vita*, 69–79.

134. Hitchcock, *Rita Levi-Montalcini: Nobel Prize Winner*, 95.

135. Rita Levi-Montalcini, *Tempo di azione* (Milan: Baldini & Castoldi, 2004), 53.

136. Rita Levi-Montalcini, *Eva era africana* (Rome: Gallucci, 2005), 27–32.

137. Levi-Montalcini, *La clessidra della vita*, 69–79.

138. Calissano, *Rita Levi-Montalcini. La vita fra i neuroni*, 95.

139. Rita Levi Montalcini, *Il tuo futuro. Consigli di un Premio Nobel ai giovani* (Milan: Garzanti, 1993).

140. Rita Levi-Montalcini, *La galassia mente* (Milan: Baldini Castoldi, 1999).

141. Rita Levi-Montalcini, *Tempo di mutamenti* (Milan: Baldini Castoldi, 2002).

142. Rita Levi-Montalcini, *Tempo di azione* (Milan: Baldini Castoldi, 2004).

143. Rita Levi-Montalcini, *Tempo di revisione* (Milan: Baldini Castoldi, 2006).

144. Levi-Montalcini, *Abbi il coraggio di conoscere.*

145. Rita Levi-Montalcini, with Giuseppina Tripodi, *Rita Levi-Montalcini racconta la scuola ai ragazzi* (Milan: Fabbri Editori, 2007).

146. Rita Levi-Montalcini, with Giuseppina Tripodi, *I nuovi magellani nell'er@ digitale* (Milan: Rizzoli, 2006).

147. Rita Levi-Montalcini, with Giuseppina Tripodi, *L'altra parte del mondo* (Milan: Rizzoli, 2009).

148. Levi-Montalcini, *Cronologia di una scoperta.*

149. Calissano, *Rita Levi-Montalcini. La vita fra i neuroni*, 97–102.

150. Yount, *Rita Levi-Montalcini: Discoverer of Nerve Growth Factor*, 105.

CHAPTER TWELVE: AN ENLIGHTENED ATTITUDE TO AGING

151. Vai, *Rita Levi-Montalcini. Una donna libera*, 285.

152. William Butler Yeats, "Sailing to Byzantium," *The Collected Poems of W. B. Yeats* (London: Palgrave Macmillan, 1989), 572.

153. Marco Tullio Cicerone. *Saper invecchiare (De senectute)* (Rome: Viviani Editore, 1994), 43.

154. Levi-Montalcini, *Abbi il coraggio di conoscere*, 84, and Rita Levi-Montalcini, *L'asso nella manica a brandelli* (Milan: Baldini & Castoldi, 1998), 145.

155. Simone de Beauvoir, *La terza età* (Turin: Einaudi, 1970), 494.

156. Vai, *Rita Levi-Montalcini. Una donna libera*, 294.

157. Dennis J. Selkoe, *L'invecchiamento cerebrale e i disturbi della memoria* (Milan: La Scienza, 1992), 107–108.

158. McGrayne, *Nobel Prize Women in Science*, 36.

159. Cristiana Pulcinelli and Tina Simoniello, *Rita Levi-Montalcini*, 124.

EPILOGUE: THE LEGACY OF RITA LEVI-MONTALCINI

160. Vai, *Rita Levi-Montalcini. Una donna libera*, 127.

161. Levi-Montalcini, *Cantico di una vita*, 32.

162. The Russell-Einstein Manifesto, July 9 1955

163. Ibid., p.106.

Chronology

April 22, 1909	Rita Levi-Montalcini is born in Turin, Italy.
October 1922	King Victor Emmanuel III appoints Benito Mussolini Prime Minister of Italy.
June 10, 1924	Death of Italian Socialist Party leader Giacomo Matteotti. Rise of fascism in Italy.
September 1930	Rita enrolls at the University of Turin School of Medicine under Professor Giuseppe Levi.
November 1930	Death of Giovanna Bruatto, the Levi-Montalcinis' governess, who inspires Rita to dedicate her life to medicine.
August 1, 1932	Death of Adamo Levi, Rita's father.
June 1936	Rita graduates from Turin School of Medicine summa cum laude in medicine and surgery.

June 1936	Rita enrolls in a three-year specialization course in neurology and psychiatry at the Clinic for Nervous and Mental Diseases in Turin.
July 14, 1938	"The Racial Manifesto" against the Jews, signed by ten so-called scientists, is published in Italian newspapers.
October 16, 1938	Government proclaims that Jewish people are forbidden to study or work in the universities or academies of Italy.
March– December 1939	Rita and members of her family live in Brussels.
September 12, 1939	Germany invades Poland.
May 1939	Pact of Steel: Italy becomes a war ally of Germany.
June 10, 1940	Italy declares war against France and Great Britain.
Summer 1940	Viktor Hamburger's landmark 1934 article about the nervous system in chicken embryos inspires Rita.
Fall 1941	Rita creates a laboratory in her tiny bedroom and performs experiments on chick embryos. Professor Levi joins her.
Winter 1941	The Allies bomb Turin. The Levi-Montalcini family moves to the hills near Asti. Rita continues to experiment on chick embryos.

September 8, 1943	The armistice with the Allies during the Second World War is secretly signed.
September 10, 1943	German tanks invade Turin.
October 8, 1943	The Levi-Montalcinis try to flee to Switzerland, but end up hiding in Florence.
September 2, 1944	British troops liberate Florence.
September 1944– July 1945	Rita reclaims her identity and works as a medical doctor in war-torn Italy.
May 8, 1945	End of the Second World War. Rita resumes work at the University of Turin.
September 19, 1947	Rita leaves Italy, joins the laboratory team of embryologist Viktor Hamburger at Washington University, St. Louis, Missouri.
January 1950	Rita learns of Elmer Bueker's experiments using mouse sarcoma cells to induce nerve growth in chick embryos.
December 1950	Rita observes cell migration and death in chick embryo nervous system.
December 1951	Rita presents her new findings at the New York Academy of Sciences.
September 1952	Rita travels to Rio de Janeiro to work in vitro at the laboratory of Hertha Meyer.
January 1953	Rita returns to Washington University and begins collaboration with biochemist Stanley Cohen.

September 1956	Rita, with Stanley Cohen, announces discovery of the nerve growth factor. Rita is appointed associate professor at Washington University. Rita is granted American citizenship with the name of Levi-Montalcini.
1958	Rita is appointed full professor at Washington University.
June 1959	Stanley Cohen leaves Washington University.
Spring 1961	Rita establishes the Laboratory of Cell Biology in Rome.
1969	Rita is awarded the Antonio Feltrinelli Prize by the Accademia Nazionale dei Lincei, Rome.
1969–1972	With Luigi Aloe, Rita begins studying the nervous system of insects.
1977	Rita retires from Washington University. Receives first honorary degree, Uppsala University, Sweden.
1978	Rita receives honorary degree, Weizmann Institute of Science, Rehovot, Israel.
July 1979	Rita retires from the Laboratory of Cell Biology.
1980	Rita receives honorary degree, St. Mary's College and University of Notre Dame, Indiana.

1982   Rita receives honorary degree, Washington University Medical School, St. Louis, Missouri.

October 13, 1986   The Nobel Foundation announces joint award of 1986 Nobel Prize for Physiology or Medicine to Rita Levi-Montalcini and Stanley Cohen.

December 10, 1986   Rita's Nobel Prize ceremony, Stockholm, Sweden.

1987   Rita receives honorary degree, University of London, England.

Rita receives honorary degree, University of Buenos Aires, Argentina.

Rita receives honorary degree, Loyola University of Chicago, Illinois.

Rita receives honorary degree, Institute of Biophysics Carlos Chagas Filho, Rio de Janeiro, Brazil.

1988   Publication of *In Praise of Imperfection*, Rita's autobiography.

1989   Rita receives honorary degree, Harvard University, Cambridge, Massachusetts.

1990   Rita receives honorary degree, Università di Urbino, Italy.

1991   Rita receives honorary degree, Università di Trieste, Italy.

Rita receives honorary degree, Università di Siena, Italy.

1992	Rita establishes the Levi-Montalcini Onlus Foundation with her twin sister, Paola.
	Rita receives honorary degree, Constantinian University, Rhode Island, New England.
1993	Publication of Rita's book *Il tuo futuro*.
	Rita receives honorary citizenship from the city of Catanzaro, Italy.
1998	Rita receives honorary degree, Università degli Studi di Palermo, Italy.
	Rita receives honorary degree, University of Cambridge, England.
1999	Rita becomes Ambassador of the Food and Agricultural Organization.
2000	Rita receives honorary degree, Hebrew University of Jerusalem, Israel.
September 28, 2000	Paola, Rita's twin sister, dies.
2001	Rita is appointed a life senator of the Italian Republic.
	Publication of Rita's book *Un universo inquieto*.
	Rita receives honorary degree, Università di Bologna, Italy.
2002	Founds the European Brain Research Institute (EBRI) in Rome, Italy.
	Publication of Rita's book *Tempo di mutamenti*.

2002   Rita receives honorary degree, Università degli Studi di Ferrara, Italy.

2004   Rita receives honorary degree, Università degli Studi del Sannio, Benevento, Italy.

2005   Rita receives honorary degree, Medicinae Barcinonensis Academia, Barcelona, Spain.

Rita becomes an honorary academic, Accademia Internazionale Partenopea Federico II, Naples, Italy.

2006   Rita receives honorary degree, Università degli Studi di Perugia, Italy.

Rita is awarded Commandeur de la Légion d'Honneur, Paris, France.

Rita receives honorary degree, Politecnico di Torino, Italy.

2008   Rita receives honorary degree, Università degli studi di Milano-Bicocca, Milan, Italy.

Rita receives honorary doctorate, Complutense University, Madrid, Spain.

Rita is presented with the Gold Medal of the French Academy by Frédéric Mitterand, Villa Medici, Rome.

2011	Rita receives honorary degree, McGill University, Montreal, Quebec, Canada, presented at Sapienza Università di Roma.
December 30, 2012	Rita dies in her Roman apartment.

Bibliography

Books by Rita Levi-Montalcini

Il messaggio nervoso. With Pietro Angeletti and Giuseppe Moruzzi. Milan: Rizzoli, 1975.

Elogio dell'imperfezione. Milan: Garzanti, 1987.

In Praise of Imperfection: My Life and Work. Translated by Luigi Attardi. New York: Basic Books Inc., 1988.

NGF: Apertura di una nuova frontiera nella neurobiologia. Rome: Theoria, 1989.

Il tuo futuro. Consigli di un Premio Nobel ai giovani. Milan: Garzanti, 1993.

Senz'olio contro vento. Milan: Baldini & Castoldi, 1996.

The Saga of the Nerve Growth Factor: Preliminary Studies, Discovery, Further Development. Vol. 3. Singapore: World Scientific, 1997.

L'asso nella manica a brandelli. Milan: Baldini & Castoldi, 1998.

La galassia mente. Milan: Baldini Castoldi Dalai, 1999.

Cantico di una vita. Milan: R. Cortina (Ed.), 2000.

Un universo inquieto. Vita e opere di Paola Levi-Montalcini. Milan: Baldini Castoldi Dalai, 2001.

Tempo di mutamenti. Milan: Baldini & Castoldi, 2002.

Tempo di azione. Milan: Baldini Castoldi Dalai, 2004.

Abbi il coraggio di conoscere. Milan: Rizzoli, 2004.

Eva era africana. Rome: Gallucci, 2005.

Tempo di revisione. Milan: Baldini Castoldi Dalai, 2006.

I nuovi magellani nell'er@ digitale. With Giuseppina Tripodi. Milan: Rizzoli, 2006.

Rita Levi-Montalcini racconta la scuola ai ragazzi. With Giuseppina Tripodi. Milan: Fabbri Editori, 2007.

Ritmi d'arte. Brescia: Serra Tarantola, 2008.

La clessidra della vita. With Giuseppina Tripodi. Milan: Baldini Castoldi Dalai, 2008.

Le tue antenate. Donne pioniere nella società e nella scienza dall'antichità ai giorni nostri. With Giuseppina Tripodi. Rome: Gallucci, 2008.

Cronologia di una scoperta. Milan: Baldini Castoldi Dalai, 2009.

L'altra parte del mondo. With Giuseppina Tripodi. Milan: Rizzoli, 2009.

NGF La molecola della vita. Roma: Treccani, 2019.

Journal Articles by Rita Levi-Montalcini

Levi-Montalcini, Rita, and Giuseppe Levi. "Correlazioni nello sviluppo tra varie parti del sistema nervoso." *Acta Pontificia Academia Scientiarum* (1945).

Levi-Montalcini, Rita, and Viktor Hamburger. "Selective growth-stimulating effects of mouse sarcoma on the sensory and sympathetic system of the chick embryo." *Journal of Experimental Zoology* (1951).

Cohen, Stanley, Rita Levi-Montalcini, and Viktor Hamburger. "A nerve growth-stimulating factor isolated from sarcomas 37 and 180." *Proceedings of the National Academy of Sciences of the United States of America* (1954).

Levi-Montalcini, Rita, and Stanley Cohen. "In vitro and in vivo effects of a nerve growth stimulating agent isolated from snake venom." *Proceedings of the National Academy of Sciences of the United States of America* (1956).

Levi-Montalcini, Rita, and Stanley Cohen. "Effects of the extract of the mouse submaxillary salivary glands on the sympathetic system of mammals." *Annals of the New York Academy of Sciences* (1960).

Levi-Montalcini, Rita, and Pietro Angeletti. "Nerve growth factor." *Physiological Reviews* (1968).

Aloe, Luigi, and Rita Levi-Montalcini. "Interrelation and dynamic activity of visceral muscle and nerve cells from insect embryos in long-term culture." *Journal of Neurobiology* (1972).

Aloe, Luigi, and Rita Levi-Montalcini. "Nerve growth factor-induced transformation of immature chromaffin cells in vivo into sympathetic neurons: effects of antiserum to nerve growth factor." *Proceedings of the National Academy of Sciences of the United States of America* (1979).

Calissano, Pietro, and Rita Levi-Montalcini. "Is NGF an enzyme?" *Nature* (1979).

Aloe, Luigi, Enrico Alleva, Ariela Bohm, and Rita Levi-Montalcini. "Aggressive behaviour induces release of nerve growth factor mouse salivary gland into the bloodstream." *Proceedings of the National Academy of Sciences of the United States of America* (1986).

Lambiase, Alessandro, Luigi Aloe, M. Centofanti, V. Parisi, and Rita Levi-Montalcini. "Experimental and clinical evidence of neuroprotection by nerve growth factor eye drops: Implications for glaucoma." *Proceedings of the National Academy of Sciences of the United States of America* (2009).

Works by Other Authors

Badoglio, Pietro. *L'Italia nella seconda guerra mondiale.* Milan: Mondadori, 1946.

Battifoglia, Enrica. *Rita Levi-Montalcini. L'irresistibile fascino del cervello.* Milan: Hoepli, 2018.

Bobbio, Norberto. *De senectute e altri scritti autobiografici.* Turin: Einaudi, 1996.

Calissano, Pietro. *Rita Levi-Montalcini. La vita fra i neuroni.* Florence: Edizioni Clichy, 2017.

Capriolo, Paola. *Rita Levi-Montalcini. Una vita per la conoscenza.* San Dorligo della Valle (TS): Edizioni EL, 2017.

Ciano, Galeazzo. *Diario 1939–43.* Milan: Rizzoli, 1947.

Cicerone, Marco Tullio. *Saper invecchiare (De senectute)*. Rome: Viviani Editore, 1994.

De Beauvoir, Simone. *La terza età*. Turin: Einaudi, 1970.

De Felice, Renzo. *The Jews in Fascist Italy: A History*. New York: Enigma Books, 2015.

Doidge, Norman. *The Brain That Changes Itself*. New York: Penguin Books, 2007.

Garlando, Luigi, in conversation with Luigi Aloe. *Mosche, cavallette, scarafaggi e premio Nobel*. Milan: HarperCollins, 2019.

Ginzburg, Natalia. *Lessico famigliare*. Turin: Einaudi, 1963.

Gramsci, Antonio. *Note sul Machiavelli, sulla politica e sullo stato moderno*. Turin: Einaudi, 1949.

Hitchcock, Susan Tyler. *Rita Levi-Montalcini: Nobel Prize Winner*. Philadelphia: Chelsea House Publishers, 2004.

Levi, Carlo. Introduction by Italo Calvino. *Cristo si è fermato a Eboli*. Turin: Einaudi, 1945.

Levi, Primo. *Se questo è un uomo*. Turin: Einaudi, 1947.

Levi, Primo. *Se non ora, quando?* Turin: Einaudi, 1982.

Luria, Salvador E. *A Slot Machine, A Broken Test Tube: An Autobiography*. New York: Harper & Row, 1984.

McGrayne, Sharon Bertsch. *Nobel Prize Women in Science: Their Lives, Struggles, and Momentous Discoveries*. Washington, D.C.: Joseph Henry Press, 2001.

Morante, Elsa. *History*. New York: Alfred Knopf, 1977.

Pulcinelli, Cristiana, and Tina Simoniello. *Rita Levi-Montalcini*. Rome: L'Asino d'oro, 2014.

Ruskin, John. *Sesame and Lilies*. London: Dent, 1907.

Russel, Bertrand A. W., *The Russell-Einstein Manifesto*, 1955.

Samson, Fred. *The Neurosciences: Paths of Discovery II*. Boston: Birkhäuser, 1992.

Snowdon, David. *Aging with Grace*. New York: Bantam Books, 2001.

Toraldo, Manfredi, and Francesco Mobili. *Rita Levi-Montalcini. Una donna di frontiera*. Rome: Senato della Repubblica and Fondazione EBRI Rita Levi-Montalcini, 2016.

Toraldo, Manfredi, and Francesco Mobili. *Rita Levi-Montalcini. A Pioneer in Neuroscience*. Translated by Pina Moliterno. Rome: Italian Senate and EBRI Rita Levi-Montalcini Foundation, 2016.

Tripodi, Giuseppina. *L'istruzione chiave dello sviluppo*. Milan: Baldini Castoldi Dalai, 2004.

Vai, Carola. *Rita Levi-Montalcini. Una donna libera*. Soveria Mannelli: Rubbettino, 2019.

Yeats, William Butler. Edited by Roberto Sanesi. *Poesie*. Milan: Lerici, 1961.

Yeats, William Butler. Edited by Richard J. Finneran. *The Collected Poems of W. B. Yeats*. London: Palgrave Macmillan, 1989.

Yount, Lisa. *Rita Levi-Montalcini: Discoverer of Nerve Growth Factor*. New York: Chelsea House Publishers, 2009.

About the Author

Francesca Valente was the director of several Italian Cultural Institutes (ICI) in North America for over thirty years, during which she distinguished herself as a cultural mediator, art curator, and translator. While in San Francisco in the early eighties she organized, among other major events in the western United States, a unique exhibition of Leonardo da Vinci drapery studies, once owned by Giorgio Vasari, which traveled to eleven university museums starting in Berkeley and ending in Princeton. She also presented the work of major twentieth-century masters at the San Francisco Museum of Modern Art as well as the work of young emerging artists at the ICI.

City Lights published an iconic volume of P. P. Pasolini's poems that Francesca translated along with Lawrence Ferlinghetti, with a preface by Alberto Moravia.

She translated into Italian essays by Frank Lloyd Wright; novels and poems by Margaret Atwood and Leonard Cohen; short stories by Alice Munro, Barry Callaghan, and Leon Rooke; and a number of nonfiction books by Northrop Frye and Marshall McLuhan. She also translated into English poems by Giorgio Bassani and Patrizia Cavalli.

While posted in Rome, she was responsible for the Culture and Heritage Department at the UNESCO National Commission for Italy, co-curated the collection of contemporary art of the Italian Ministry of Foreign Affairs (MAE), and was appointed as the cultural liaison between MAE and the City of Venice. Back in North America, she showcased major Italian contemporary artists in several museums and cultural institutions. She facilitated the donation and installation of a mosaic by Alighiero Boetti at California State University, Northridge; a sculpture by Eliseo Mattiacci at the sculpture garden of the University of California, Los Angeles; and a monumental fountain by Enzo Cucchi at York University, Toronto.

In her most recent post in Los Angeles, she conceived and organized a breakthrough exhibition entitled *Leonardo da Vinci and Bill Viola* at the ICI that paired their works.

After concluding her career with the Italian Ministry of Foreign Affairs, she was invited by the Italian government to coordinate the eighty-nine Italian Cultural Institutes throughout the world for the 2011 Padiglione Italia, Biennale Arte, Venice.

During 2016–18 she curated an exhibition of 220 artists from central and eastern Canada and the US for *Imago Mundi*, Luciano Benetton Foundation, featured at Palazzo Loredan, Venice, and at OCAD University Onsite Gallery, Toronto, Canada.

In 2018–19 she curated two exhibitions of California artist Nancy Genn at Palazzo Ferro Fini and the Ca' Pesaro gallery, Venice.

She recently published *A. P. Giannini: The People's Banker* in a bilingual edition for the Mentoris Project, Los Angeles, reviewed by Gian Antonio Stella in *Corriere della Sera* and Marco Onado in *Il Sole 24 Ore*.

Acknowledgments

I wish to thank Piera Levi-Montalcini for the useful information on Rita's private life; Roberto Capucci for his insightful anecdotes; Luigi Aloe and Pietro Calissano for their generous availability and knowledge. Special thanks also to Giuliano Gori for guiding me in fruitful directions in my research in Italy.

I would like to express my gratitude to Janice Keefer and Jane Varnus for helping co-edit my ebook. I would love to extend my heartfelt thanks to Tania Moretto for the precious help in compiling the chronology and bibliography; Filippo Mariano, Laura Pietropaolo, Maria Lella Rebecchini, Rosemary Sullivan, Michelle Tripodi and David Wistow for being very supportive of my project; Branko and Francesco Valente-Gorjup, my husband and son, for being next to me from the beginning.

Above all, I would like to thank Rita, who was my inspiration and spiritual companion during the COVID-19 pandemic, for leaving the most engaging pages about her life, a Nobel honoring Italy, and an example to follow for all young people interested in science.

Building Wealth 101
How to Make Your Money Work For You
by Robert Barbera

Christopher Columbus: His Life and Discoveries
by Mario Di Giovanni

Dark Labyrinth
A Novel Based on the Life of Galileo Galilei
by Peter David Myers

Defying Danger
A Novel Based on the Life of Father Matteo Ricci
by Nicole Gregory

The Divine Proportions of Luca Pacioli
A Novel Based on the Life of Luca Pacioli
by W. A. W. Parker

Dreams of Discovery
A Novel Based on the Life of the Explorer John Cabot
by Jule Selbo

The Faithful
A Novel Based on the Life of Giuseppe Verdi
by Collin Mitchell

Fermi's Gifts
A Novel Based on the Life of Enrico Fermi
by Kate Fuglei

First Among Equals
A Novel Based on the Life of Cosimo de' Medici
by Francesco Massaccesi

God's Messenger
The Astounding Achievements of Mother Cabrini
A Novel Based on the Life of Mother Frances X. Cabrini
by Nicole Gregory

Grace Notes
A Novel Based on the Life of Henry Mancini
by Stacia Raymond

Harvesting the American Dream
A Novel Based on the Life of Ernest Gallo
by Karen Richardson

Humble Servant of Truth
A Novel Based on the Life of Thomas Aquinas
by Margaret O'Reilly

Leonardo's Secret
A Novel Based on the Life of Leonardo da Vinci
by Peter David Myers

Little by Little We Won
A Novel Based on the Life of Angela Bambace
by Peg A. Lamphier, PhD

The Making of a Prince
A Novel Based on the Life of Niccolò Machiavelli
by Maurizio Marmorstein

A Man of Action Saving Liberty
A Novel Based on the Life of Giuseppe Garibaldi
by Rosanne Welch, PhD

Marconi and His Muses
A Novel Based on the Life of Guglielmo Marconi
by Pamela Winfrey

No Person Above the Law
A Novel Based on the Life of Judge John J. Sirica
by Cynthia Cooper

Relentless Visionary: Alessandro Volta
A Biography by Michael Berick

Ride Into the Sun
A Novel Based on the Life of Scipio Africanus
by Patric Verrone

Saving the Republic
A Novel Based on the Life of Marcus Cicero
by Eric D. Martin

Soldier, Diplomat, Archaeologist
A Novel Based on the Bold Life of Louis Palma di Cesnola
by Peg A. Lamphier, PhD

The Soul of a Child
A Novel Based on the Life of Maria Montessori
by Kate Fuglei

What a Woman Can Do
A Novel Based on the Life of Artemisia Gentileschi
by Peg A. Lamphier, PhD

FUTURE TITLES FROM THE MENTORIS PROJECT

Novels Based on the Lives of:

Amerigo Vespucci
Andrea Doria
Antonin Scalia
Antonio Meucci
Buzzie Bavasi
Cesare Beccaria
Father Eusebio Francisco Kino
Federico Fellini
Frank Capra
Guido d'Arezzo
Harry Warren
Leonardo Fibonacci
Maria Gaetana Agnesi
Peter Rodino
Pietro Belluschi
Saint Augustine of Hippo
Saint Francis of Assisi
Vince Lombardi

For more information on these titles and
the Mentoris Project, please visit
www.mentorisproject.org